Practical Parenting

Kathy Sammis

illustrated by Roz Davis

 J. Weston Walch, Publisher

Portland, Maine

1   2   3   4   5   6   7   8   9   10

ISBN 0-8251-2089-6

Copyright © 1992
J. Weston Walch, Publisher
P.O. Box 658 • Portland, Maine 04104-0658

Printed in the United States of America

Contents

Introduction

When you are a parent or a caregiver in charge of a baby or young child, you have a great responsibility. You must give your baby or child the physical care she can't provide for herself—you have to dress her, keep her clean, give her a home. You also must feed your baby or child the food she needs to grow strong and healthy. You have to keep your baby or child safe and healthy, and care for her when she's sick.

As a parent or caregiver, you also have to guide your baby or child's behavior; you must teach him how to behave and how to direct his actions by himself. In addition, you have a responsibility to help your baby or child learn the many physical and mental skills he needs to develop as he grows up.

When you need substitute care for your baby or young child, you'll need to find a person or center that can effectively take over all these responsibilities for you while you're not with your child.

This is an awesome range of responsibilities! That's why we designed this *Practical Parenting* workbook—to show you simple, clear, effective ways to do all these things for your baby or young child. In these pages, you'll find parenting tips, explanations, guidelines, activities, and exercises. When you're through with the workbook, you'll feel confident and knowledgeable about your role as a parent or caregiver.

PHYSICAL CARE, HEALTH, AND SAFETY

Babies and young children depend on their parents and caregivers for the most basic needs: food, clothing, shelter, cleanliness, safety from harm, care during illness. When you are a parent or caregiver, you *must* meet these needs. Otherwise, your baby or young child can't survive.

Babies can't do much of anything for themselves. So the amount of time a parent or caregiver must spend taking care of a baby is very large.

Toddlers begin to learn how to do many things for themselves. But they still need help with just about everything. Toddler care, then, is also very time-consuming.

Preschool and kindergarten children can do many things for themselves, and they can be a help around the home. Parents and caregivers of these children find that their child-care duties are lessening.

Let's take a general look at the basic things that you, as a parent or caregiver, must provide for your young child's physical care, health, and safety. Then we'll see exactly how to do what's needed at each of three stages: the baby years, the toddler years, and the preschool and kindergarten years.

PHYSICAL CARE: WHAT YOUR BABY OR CHILD NEEDS

■ Feeding.

A baby/child needs the basic amount of food and liquids that will keep her healthy and let her mind and body grow as they should. (For feeding guidelines, see the section titled "Nutrition" later in this book.)

1

■ **Rest and sleep.**
A baby/child needs certain amounts of sleep to rest the mind and body and renew his sources of energy.

■ **Bathing and cleanliness.**
A baby/child needs to be kept clean enough to avoid illness and discomfort and to promote good health and self-esteem.

■ **Clothing and dressing.**
A baby/child needs clothing that keeps her warm enough or comfortable enough. She needs help getting into and out of her clothing.

■ **Shelter.**
A baby/child needs a home that is warm, clean, secure, and comforting.

HEALTH REQUIREMENTS

You are responsible for keeping your child healthy. You are also responsible for getting your child the medical care he needs when he is ill or injured.

To keep your baby/child healthy, follow the guidelines in this book about physical care and nutrition. Be sure your baby/child gets the immunizations he needs (see the section below). Know the common symptoms of illness and what to do about them. And be sure to talk to a health-care worker when necessary. (See "Common Health Problems" below.)

Immunizations

Immunizations, also called inoculations, are shots or liquid drops that protect your baby or young child from certain illnesses. They make your baby/child immune to the disease, which means she can't get that illness.

It's *very important* to be sure your baby gets these immunizations. The diseases they prevent could make your child extremely ill, damage his nervous system, brain and heart, or even cripple or kill your child.

Here are the immunizations your baby/child needs, and the ages when she needs them. Be sure your child gets all of these, at a doctor's office or a well-baby clinic.

THE AMERICAN ACADEMY OF PEDIATRICS RECOMMENDS THE IMMUNIZATION SCHEDULE BELOW:	
BABY'S AGE	**IMMUNIZATION**
2 Months	DTP-Diphtheria, Tetanus, Pertussis (Whooping Cough) Polio
4 Months	DTP Polio
6 Months	DTP
1 Year	Tuberculin Test
15 Months	Measles Rubella (German Measles) Mumps
18 Months	DTP Polio

Fill in the dates when your baby/child gets each immunization.

IMMUNIZATION	AGE WHEN BABY/ CHILD NEEDS IT	AGE & DATE WHEN YOUR BABY/CHILD GOT IT
DPT*	2 months	
Polio	2 months	
DPT	4 months	
Polio	4 months	
DPT	6 months	
Measles, mumps & rubella	12 months	
DPT booster	15 months	
Polio	15 months	
DPT booster	4–5 years	
Polio	5 years	

* DPT = Diphtheria, Pertussis (Whooping Cough), & Tetanus

Common Health Problems

You can expect your baby or young child to develop some common health problems. Some are minor—for instance, a mild cold, a heat rash, a slight fever.

Others are more serious—for instance, a bacterial infection, an inflamed appendix, a contagious disease.

Gradually, you'll get used to these childhood health conditions. You'll learn how to recognize symptoms—signs of a health problem or illness.

Calling for Help

When you are a new or inexperienced parent or caregiver, it's usually best to call your doctor or clinic whenever your baby/child develops a symptom you haven't seen before. After a while, you'll get to know when you need to call your doctor or clinic for advice, and when you can take care of the condition on your own.

In case of emergency, you'll need to know basic first aid. (See the "First Aid" section on pages 10–11.) You'll also have to call for medical help right away. Write the phone numbers to call here:

_____

EMERGENCY PHONE NUMBER:

(   )   -

Doctor's Phone Number: _____

Clinic Phone Number: _____

Poison Control Center Number: _____

When you call your doctor or clinic, be prepared to describe all your child's symptoms. (What is his temperature? How long has he had the stomachache? What exactly does the rash look like, and where is it? Does he have diarrhea? And so on.)

Role-Play

In class, role-play the part of an anxious parent calling a doctor's office or clinic to ask about your baby's or young child's symptoms. One student plays the part of the parent; another plays the part of a health-care worker who answers the phone. As a class, critique the role-play.

Symptoms

You'll probably find it a big help to have a paperback book at home that describes childhood illnesses. (A good, affordable one is the old favorite, Dr. Spock's *Baby and Child Care*.) Here is a list of the most common health problems and symptoms your baby/child is likely to develop.

> *Remember*: When in doubt—when you have *any* question about your baby or child's health or physical condition—call a doctor or clinic for medical advice!

■ Appetite loss.

When your child is not feeling well, she probably will lose some interest in food. That's normal. (Just be sure she drinks lots of fluids, in most cases.) Your child's appetite normally varies from day to day (see the section on "Nutrition"). But if your child has lost interest in food for several days, and she doesn't have any obvious illness that has caused the loss of appetite, talk to your doctor/clinic.

■ Common colds.

Everyone gets an occasional cold, even babies. Most young children will have as many as seven or eight colds per year. And no wonder—at least 150 different cold viruses exist!

You can't cure a cold, or make it shorter. You can only treat symptoms. If there's a lot of mucus in the nose, remove it with a nasal syringe (a soft tube with a rubber bulb on the end). Keep indoor air moist. Use cold remedies, tablets, or nose drops *only if* your doctor/clinic says they're okay. (Most don't do any good, anyway.)

Call your doctor/clinic if your baby is less than 3 months old and has a cold. If your older baby or child has a cold with only a runny nose and slight cough, you don't need medical help. Do call your doctor/clinic if your baby/child has a cold with a fever, earache, difficulty breathing, or other symptoms.

As your child gets older, he'll develop some immunity and will get fewer colds.

■ Cough and croup.

Your baby/child will probably cough a little when she has a cold. If your young baby coughs often, have your doctor/clinic check her. Also talk to your doctor/clinic if your baby/child has coughing spasms, fever, or vomiting with the cough, or if the cough lasts for several days.

Croup is an infection that causes a hoarse, tight cough. Your child will sound like a barking seal! He'll also have a lot of trouble breathing in, which is scary for him and you. Call your doctor/clinic when your child develops croup. The best treatment for it is moist air. Use a cold-air humidifier. Or run the hot water in the shower with the bathroom door closed. When the bathroom is full of steam, bring your child in and sit with him for 10 or 20 minutes. (Don't get in the hot shower, though.)

■ Diarrhea.

When your baby/child passes watery, thin bowel movements, he has diarrhea. A few loose stools and a few extra bowel movements are nothing to worry about. But if your baby/child is having a number of very loose bowel movements during the day, call your doctor/clinic.

■ Ear infection.

This is very common in young children. A child who can talk will tell you her ear hurts. A baby who can't talk will scream and pull at his ear. Call your doctor/clinic for advice.

■ Fever.

You need to learn how to take your baby/child's temperature. Ask your health-care worker to show you how to use and read a fever thermometer. Call your doctor/clinic if your baby/child's temperature is 101°F or higher. (A fever below 104°F isn't *necessarily* dangerous, but you need to know.)

■ Skin rash.

Skin rashes are very common, and it is very hard to tell what's causing one. You need to consult your doctor/clinic. Be prepared to describe the rash in detail. Chicken pox is a common cause of rash in preschoolers. (See the section on young children's health on page 35.)

■ Sore throat.

A child who can talk will tell you when his throat is sore. A baby with a sore throat will probably refuse to eat or cry during feedings. Look down her throat with a flashlight A sore throat will be bright red.

■ Stomachache.

Many, many things can cause stomachache. If your child complains of stomachache for more than an hour, call your doctor/clinic. (A baby with stomachache will be fussy and obviously uncomfortable.)

■ Vomiting.

When most of the stomach's contents are forced up and shoot out of the mouth, it's called vomiting. When just a spoonful or two of the stomach's contents come up and spill or dribble out of the mouth, it's called spitting up. Spitting up is very common in babies, and is nothing to worry about. If your baby/child vomits several times, call your doctor/clinic for advice.

Call your doctor/clinic if a sore throat lasts more than a day, or if your baby/child also has a fever. Although most sore throats are caused by colds, some are caused by strep bacteria and need to be treated with special medicine.

ACTIVITY

Matching

Write the name of each health problem listed below in the blank next to its symptoms.

ear infection	appetite loss	vomiting
croup	sore throat	common cold
diarrhea	skin rash	fever

1. Baby cries during feeding. _____

2. A lot of food from the stomach shoots out the mouth. _____

3. Young child sounds like a barking seal. _____

4. Child's forehead is hot to the touch. _____

5. The skin is covered with little red spots. _____

(continued)

6. Baby pulls at his ear. _____

7. Child has a runny nose. _____

8. Child has no interest in food for several days. _____

9. Baby has a lot of thin, watery bowel movements. _____

Where to Get Medical Care

Medical care can be expensive! If you can't afford a private doctor, other medical care should be available for your baby/child. The important thing is to have a regular and reliable source of medical care so you can get the help you need when you need it.

- A pediatrician is a doctor who specializes in taking care of babies and children. A pediatrician may have his or her own "private" practice, or his or her practice may be at a clinic or hospital.

- A well-baby clinic is a medical office you can use for routine health checkups of your baby and for advice when you have questions. Well-baby clinics are cheaper than private doctors. Also, clinics may charge for their services based on what you can afford to pay.

ACTIVITY

Your Community Child Care

To find medical care you can afford in your area, try contacting the services listed below. What kind of baby/child care do they offer? At what price?

Community Health Services

    Phone number: _____

    Care available: _____

    Cost of care: _____

Public Health Nursing

    Phone number: _____

    Care available: _____

    Cost of care: _____

Your Local Hospital(s): _____

    Phone number(s): _____

    Care available: _____

    Cost of care: _____

Other—Name: _____

    Phone number: _____

    Care available: _____

    Cost of care: _____

SAFETY

You are responsible for your child's safety. A baby or young child is surrounded by hazards. She doesn't know what's dangerous, though. She depends totally on you to make her world safe for her. You have three main concerns about safety.

In-Home Hazards

You'll need to arrange your home to make it safe for your baby, then your toddler, and finally your preschooler.

Out-of-Home Hazards

The older your baby/child gets, the more dangers he faces outside your home. You have to be aware of these hazards and guard against them.

First Aid

It's your duty as a parent or caregiver to know some very basic first aid. You could save your child's life by knowing what to do before medical help gets to you! Call your local Red Cross, YWCA, or YMCA to find out about basic first-aid courses in your area. These are the very important medical emergencies you need to know how to handle:

■ Bleeding.
In case of heavy bleeding, put a clean cloth over the wound and press firmly to stop the bleeding. When the bleeding stops, put a bandage over the cut. Call a doctor.

■ Breathing stops/drowning.
Begin mouth-to-mouth breathing right away. You need to take a first-aid course to learn how to do this. Have someone else call the rescue squad.

■ Broken bone.
Keep all weight off the broken part. Tie the body part to something stiff so the broken bone can't move. If a bone sticks out, stop the bleeding, then cover the bone and the wound with a bandage. Get medical help!

■ Burn.

Put the burned part under cold water, right away, for 10 minutes. Do *not* apply butter or burn ointment. See a doctor.

■ Choking.

If your baby can't cough or breathe, you must clear his throat right away. Call the emergency rescue service immediately. Turn your baby over on his stomach, and lay him on your thigh, with his head pointing down. With the heel of your hand, thump him firmly 3 or 4 times between the shoulderblades. Keeping his head towards the floor, turn him over on on his back. Place your first 2 fingers on his breastbone. Push down quickly 3 or 4 times. Repeat these steps until your baby coughs up the object or begins to breathe or cry. The best way to learn what to do for a choking baby is to take a first-aid course.

■ Head injury.

Stop any bleeding. Call a doctor right away if your baby/child is confused, sleepy, unconscious, or vomiting, or if he can't remember what happened.

■ Poisoning.

Call the Poison Control Center *right away*. Do what they tell you. Wash poisoned eyes and skin completely with water.

■ Seizure (convulsion).

(Your child's body stiffens, her arms and legs jerk, and she becomes unconscious.) Clear the area of any objects. Loosen her tight clothing if you can. *Do not* try to stop your child's movements. *Do not* force anything into her mouth or try to hold her tongue.

You also need to know what to do for routine, non-emergency medical problems—like bites or sprains. Keep a good basic first-aid or child-care book on hand.

ACTIVITY

Home First-Aid Kit

In class, brainstorm a list of basic first-aid supplies every home with babies and young children should have. Write the class list here:

_____

_____

_____

_____

_____

_____

_____

_____

_____

_____

_____

Extra Credit

Take a basic first-aid course. Share your new knowledge with your classmates in a presentation.

Physical Care, Health, and Safety for Your Baby (Age: Birth to 1 Year)

You have to do everything for your baby. She can't do much of anything for herself. Even when she's old enough to sit up, crawl, and stand, she can't dress herself, or bathe herself, or keep herself safe in any way. She depends totally on you for all aspects of her care and safety. That's why it takes so much time to take care of a baby!

PHYSICAL CARE FOR YOUR BABY

Feeding

There's so much to know about feeding your baby, we've got a whole separate section in this book about it. See the "Nutrition" section.

Handling

A new baby may seem very fragile to you. He's so small and helpless! But he's not delicate. Even the "soft spot" on top of his head is protected by a tough membrane. So don't be afraid to hold and cuddle your baby—he needs lots of loving human contact.

Just be careful of one thing: Your baby can't hold his head up. So you *always* need to support his head when you pick him up or as you put him down or hand him to someone else. Be sure his head is supported and can't fall backward when you're holding him, too.

Practice Handling

Using a doll, practice handling a baby while always supporting the baby's head. Pick up the lying "baby" and bring her up to your shoulder. Then lie the "baby" back down. Hand the "baby" to a classmate. Take the "baby" as a classmate hands her to you.

Diapers

■ Diaper changes.

How often do you change a baby's diaper?

- Change a diaper as soon as possible after a bowel movement. Clean all traces of the bowel movement off your baby's skin, using a damp cotton ball. Be sure to get all the creases of her skin!

- Change a wet diaper if your baby is fussing about it, or if you're picking her up and she's soaked through. You don't need to wash the baby's bottom each time you change a wet (not soiled with a bowel movement) diaper. (But see "Diaper Rash" below.)

■ Diaper rash.

Small, red pimples and rough, red skin in your baby's diaper area is called diaper rash. It's quite common, because your baby's skin is sensitive.

If your baby develops diaper rash, ask your doctor or clinic what kind of protective ointment to use. Stop using waterproof pants or plastic-covered disposable diapers for a while. Wash off the baby's skin after every diaper change.

■ Kinds of diapers.

Basically, you have three choices for diapers: disposables, diapers from a service, or wash-your-own.

TYPE OF DIAPER	ADVANTAGES	DISADVANTAGES
Disposables	Convenient Easy to use No pins Variety of sizes, shapes	Expensive May promote diaper rash Contribute to trash crisis
Diaper Service	Convenient: delivers and takes away diapers for you Less diaper rash	Expensive

Wash-your-own	Saves money
	Most comfortable for many
	   babies
		Takes time and expense to
		   wash them

ACTIVITY

Diapering Practice

Using a baby doll or (better yet) a real baby, practice changing a diaper. Use both disposable and cloth diapers so you know how to use both kinds.

ACTIVITY

Diaper Costs

Discover how diaper costs compare with each other. Assume you need 60 diapers per week for your baby.

Disposables:
Diaper Service:
Wash-Your-Own:

Sleep

You don't have to decide how much sleep your baby needs. He'll take exactly the amount of sleep he needs. Some babies sleep more, some less. A newborn sleeps most of the time. As your baby gets older, he'll sleep less and less, especially during the day. By the time he's a year old, he'll probably be taking only two naps a day. Here are some baby-sleep hints:

- Most babies can easily sleep through regular household noises. So don't try to keep your home quiet when your baby sleeps. You'll just train her to *need* quiet in order to sleep.

- Put your baby to sleep on her stomach most of the time. Then if she vomits, she's not likely to choke.

- Let your baby sleep in a different room, not in your bedroom. Just be sure he's close enough so you can hear him cry.

- Nighttime room temperature can be 60°F as long as you dress your baby in a warm-enough sleeper.

- *Never* put a pillow in your baby's crib or carriage. He could smother.

Clothing and Fresh Air

Dress your baby as warmly or lightly as other family members dress. Keep clothing comfortable, so your baby can move as much as he wants. Give your baby some fresh air almost every day: Let her sleep in her carriage outdoors, take her on outings, or open a window near her crib or carriage.

Bathing

Bathing a baby is something both a parent or caregiver and the baby have to get used to. A new baby dislikes being completely undressed. He

feels very insecure in a bathtub because he's not well supported. An inexperienced parent or caregiver feels insecure, too, trying to hold a limp, slippery baby in a tub full of water. Full tub baths aren't really necessary for the first few months. Try sponge baths instead to start.

■ Sponge bath.

Wash the parts of your baby that need cleaning, one at a time. Use soap with a wet washcloth or your hand. Rinse off *all* the soap. Be sure to get the creases of skin, and the neck area. Wash the face with clear warm water

(no soap). Be especially careful to rinse off sticky milk and dried food from face and hands. Use Baby (no-sting) shampoo for matted or dirty hair.

■Tub baths.

Here's how to get started with tub baths:

- Have everything ready, next to the bath. (You can't leave to get anything you forgot.)
- Use a soft, baby-sized tub. When your baby gets older (around 4 or 5 months), you can get him used to the big bathtub.
- Keep the room warm and the water at body temperature (comfortably warm to the touch).
- Have the tub at your waist level, or kneel down if the tub is on the floor.
- Use only an inch or two of water at first.
- Support your baby's head on your left wrist, holding his upper arm with your left hand. Your right hand is free for bathing. Ask the nurses at the hospital to show you how to do this.
- Wash as you did with the sponge bath.
- Let your baby splash and learn to have fun in the bath. Don't splash her, though! When she's a little older, she'll love floating and pouring bath toys.
- Grasp your baby *firmly* as you lift him out of the bath. (He's *very* slippery!)
- Wrap your baby in a towel and pat him dry. Be sure to dry all the creases.

Don't ever leave your baby alone in a bath even for an instant!

ACTIVITY

Practice Bathing

Using a doll and a baby bathtub, practice bathing a baby. Does it take you a while to get the hang of it?

Teething

By the time your baby is a year old, he'll probably have around eight teeth. The picture shows the *average* age when babies get their first teeth, called *incisors*, or the "front teeth." Your baby may cut her first tooth at 4 months, or at 10 months, or at some other time.

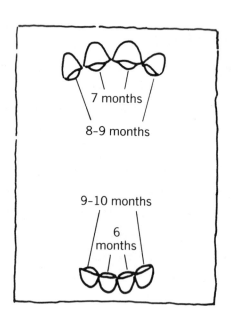

ACTIVITY

Your Baby's Teeth

Fill in the dates and ages when your baby cut each of these teeth:

2 bottom center:
2 top center:
2 top alongside center:
2 bottom alongside center:

Most babies aren't bothered by cutting these front teeth. Your baby may drool and chew a lot when teeth are coming in. Give him things to chew on.

Teething does *not* cause fever, diarrhea, colds, or other illnesses. If your baby is sick while she's teething, call your doctor or clinic as usual.

Clothing and Equipment

Visit a friend who has a baby. How can one tiny human being need so much clothing and equipment? A baby may be tiny, but he's a complicated machine who needs lots of baby-sized accessories to live in an adult world. You'll have what you need if you follow this list.

Furniture

Crib & mattress
Crib bumpers
Dresser
Changing table & pad
Playpen
High chair
Wind-up swing

Feeding

Bottles & nipples
Bottle brush
Feeding dish & spoon
Formula
Baby food
Vitamin drops
Bibs

(continued)

Clothing

Nightgowns
Stretch suits
Shirts
Sweaters
Waterproof pants
Warm sleeper

For Sitting, Carrying, and Traveling

Front (sling-type) carrier
Backpack
Infant seat
Car seat
Baby carriage (optional)
Stroller
Diaper bag (to carry all essentials whenever you go out)

Bathing and Cleaning

Baby bathtub
Soft towels & washcloths
Cotton balls
Diaper-rash ointment
Baby shampoo
Petroleum jelly
Baby nail scissors (blunt tips)
Diapers & diaper pins
Diaper pail

Bedding

Waterproof pads
Fitted crib sheets
Soft baby blankets

Miscellaneous

Cold-water vaporizer

ACTIVITY

Finding Baby Gear

Suppose a baby is going to join your family in the near future. Where in your local area could you find baby clothes and equipment cheaply? List sources below. Share lists with your classmates.

_____

_____

_____

_____

_____

_____

_____

_____

YOUR BABY'S HEALTH

Well-Baby Care

Even if your baby seems and is healthy most of the time, she needs regular medical checkups, about once a month. This is called well-baby care. You may take your baby to a private doctor or a clinic for her regular checkups. Regular well-baby care is important, so a doctor can be sure your baby is growing the way she should and is not developing any health problems.

Keep a notebook at home. Jot down any baby-care questions that occur to you between well-baby checkups. Then bring the notebook with you to the next checkup and get answers to your questions.

Immunizations

The chart on page 3 tells you what immunizations your baby needs during his first year.

ACTIVITY

What immunizations does your baby need at 2 months?

_____

What immunizations does your baby need at 4 months?

_____

What immunization does your baby need at 6 months?

_____

What immunizations does your baby need at 12 months?

_____

Symptoms

Be alert for any of the symptoms described on pages 6–8. Call your doctor or clinic when your baby is not well.

ACTIVITY

Recording Symptoms

Observe a group of babies at a child-care center, several times a week for three or four weeks. Or, observe a friend's or relative's baby for three or four weeks. Record here any symptoms you notice. If you have a baby of your own, record her symptoms.

_____

_____

_____

_____

YOUR BABY'S SAFETY

Accidents are the main cause of death for babies. Yet your baby is blissfully unaware of the many dangers that surround her. She has no idea that if she crawls over the edge of the top stair, she'll fall down the stairs and get hurt.

You can't teach your baby about safety. She's too immature to understand. So your baby's safety depends entirely on you. Keeping your baby safe is something you have to be aware of all the time. Here's a list of the most common and important safety considerations for your baby.

Falls

Never leave your baby alone on anything he could fall from, like a bed or changing table. He could roll over (even if he's never rolled over before) and off. He could push himself to the edge with his toes.

As soon as your baby can crawl, block off all stairways with gates or latched doors. Keep open windows securely screened or grated.

Water

NEVER leave your baby alone in the bath, or in a bath with a child under 5. In fact, don't leave your baby alone near *any* water, like a puddle or wading pool. A baby can drown, quickly, in an inch or two of water.

Check the temperature of your household's hot tap water. Be sure that the water that flows into your sink or tub is *not* hot enough to burn your baby.

Cribs

Your baby needs a firm mattress and no pillow, so she won't smother. The mattress must fit the crib snugly, so she can't get stuck between the mattress and crib side. Be sure the crib bars are *less than* 2¼ inches apart, so your baby can't stick her head between the bars. Use padded crib bumpers, too. Always be sure movable crib sides are securely locked into place, all the way up.

High Chairs and Infant Seats

Keep your baby securely strapped in the chair or seat. Stay near a high chair to be sure your baby doesn't tip it over. Be sure an infant seat can't tip easily. Keep an infant seat away from the edge of countertops or tables.

Toys

Your baby wants to put everything in his mouth. So you must be sure his toys have no small parts, which could come loose and be swallowed—like button eyes on stuffed animals, or metal wheels on toy cars. You don't want your baby to have any toys with sharp edges, either. And avoid plastic toys that could break apart into small, sharp pieces—like a plastic rattle.

Cars

Most states have laws that say you *must* strap your baby into a government-approved car seat, *whenever* your baby is riding in a car. Follow these laws! If you hold a baby in your lap, she'll be thrown out of your arms in an accident.

Suffocation

Keep all plastic bags out of your baby's reach! Your baby will enjoy pulling a plastic bag over his head. Then he can't breathe! Be especially careful with the thin plastic bags you bring home from the dry cleaners. Tear them, tie knots in them, throw them out right away.

Sun

Your baby's skin is very sensitive to the sun. She'll sunburn easily. Too much exposure to the sun can also promote skin cancer when your baby is grown up. So always rub sunscreen on your baby's skin when she'll be out in the sun. To be safe, use a sunscreen with an SPF (sun protection factor) of at least 15.

Baby Powder

Powdering your baby is not necessary. If you do use powder, tap it into your hand first. Then rub it on your baby. You want to be sure there's no cloud of powder in the air. It's not good for your baby's lungs if he breathes powder.

The Crawling Baby

Keep stairways closed off. Cover unused electric outlets. Keep all household products (cleansers, detergents) and medicines completely out of reach. Use place mats, not tablecloths. Be careful when you're ironing!

ACTIVITY

Safety Situations

Here are some situations a baby may be in. Decide whether each is safe or is an accident waiting to happen.

Is This Safe?

1. Your baby can't roll over yet, so you leave her in the middle of your bed while you go to answer the phone.   Safe   Unsafe

(continued)

2. Great-Aunt Drucilla has made a lovely embroidered pillow for your baby. You let your baby play with the pillow when you're watching him, but you never leave the pillow in the baby's crib.   Safe   Unsafe

3. Your baby cries to be held in the car. You keep her strapped in her baby seat.   Safe   Unsafe

4. Your baby crawls around the kitchen floor while you're ironing.   Safe   Unsafe

5. You remove the plastic bag from your dry-cleaned clothes. You put the bag in the bedroom wastebasket.   Safe   Unsafe

6. Your baby is happily eating in his high chair. You go to help your toddler in the other room for a minute.   Safe   Unsafe

7. You dress your baby in a sun bonnet and cotton top when you take her outside to play.   Safe   Unsafe

8. You tell your kindergarten child to watch his baby sister in the bath while you quickly check on the food that's cooking in the kitchen.   Safe   Unsafe

Baby-Care Review

Here are some statements about taking care of a baby. Circle *Yes* or *No* for each one.

1. Change your baby's diaper as soon as possible after a bowel movement.   Yes   No

2. Keep your home quiet while your baby is napping.   Yes   No

3. A new baby is very delicate; don't pick him up too often.   Yes   No

4. Your baby needs regular medical checkups even if she's healthy.   Yes   No

5. Your baby's bath water should be comfortably warm to the touch, not hot or cool.   Yes   No

6. A baby in your home needs lots of clothing and equipment.   Yes   No

7. Disposable diapers are better to use than wash-your-own.   Yes   No

8. Your baby needs to be kept warm, so dress him in warmer clothes than the rest of the family is wearing.   Yes   No

9. Your baby knows how much sleep she needs.   Yes   No

10. Lay your baby down on his back in the bathtub and use your hands to wash and rinse him.   Yes   No

11. Never leave your baby alone on top of anything, in a high chair, or in the bath.   Yes   No

12. Teething causes your baby to have a fever.   Yes   No

Extra: Tell what is incorrect about each of the statements you circled *No* for.

Physical Care, Health, and Safety for Your Toddler
(Age: 1 year to 3 years)

Your toddler is beginning to learn to do things for himself. But he is still much too young to know what he needs to do to take care of himself. He needs your constant help and guidance.

PHYSICAL CARE FOR YOUR TODDLER

Dressing and Bathing

Your toddler may feel strongly about her clothes. Offer her a simple choice. ("Do you want to wear the green shirt or the yellow shirt?") Let her help dress herself.

Your toddler is a dedicated explorer. Expect her to be a grubby mess by day's end. Plan on an evening bath as part of the daily routine. Most toddlers love baths, because they love water play. (But she may develop a fear of the water draining out of the tub.)

Dress your toddler in simple, cheap clothes. He'll outgrow them before he wears them out. The clothes will *always* need washing. Choose washable, no-iron fabrics. Even parkas and sweaters should be machine-washable.

Toilet Training

Every parent/caregiver looks forward to the day of the last diaper change! But you can't rush it. A young child is not physically able to control bowels and bladder. She has no interest in control, either. If you try to toilet train your toddler before she's ready and able to cooperate, you're doomed to failure.

Instead, wait until your toddler shows some interest in being dry and some awareness of his bowel and bladder movements—probably when he's around 1½ or 2 years old. Then introduce him to the potty seat.

- Introduce the potty seat gradually. Show it to your toddler. Tell her what it's for. Let her sit on it when she's fully dressed.

- Once she's used to the potty seat, lead her to it when she's not wearing a diaper and may be ready for a bowel movement. *Suggest* she try it. If she says no, try again another time or day.

- Be casual. Never force your toddler to sit on the pottty. Let potty use be *his* idea, not yours. Remember, at this age, he's programmed *not* to do whatever you suggest.

- Respect your toddler's fears about the toilet.

  —The adult toilet is very scary for many toddlers. Use a potty chair on the floor instead.

  —Flushing alarms many toddlers. It's as if their arm or leg were being flushed away. Flush later, after your toddler has left the bathroom.

- Expect it to take time. Expect it to happen at a different age for each child. Above all, expect wetting- or messing-the-pants accidents!

- Nightime dryness comes last—usually by the age of 3, but often later.

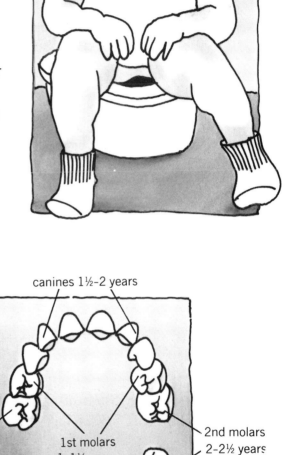

Teething

Your toddler will continue to cut teeth, at approximately these stages:

canines 1½–2 years

2nd molars 2–2½ years

1st molars 1–1½ years

2nd molars 2–2½ years

canines 1½–2 years

Your Toddler's Teeth

Fill in the dates and ages when your toddler cuts each of these teeth:

Canines:
First molars:
Second molars:

Cutting the first four molars is likely to make your toddler uncomfortable. She'll be cranky, wake up crying, lose her appetite. Give her a rubber teething ring to chew on, especially one that's been cooled in the refrigerator. Ice cubes to chew on can help, too. So can massaging the swollen gum.

Brush your toddler's teeth after each meal once she's cut her first molars. Let her brush, too. But she won't be skilled enough to get the teeth really clean. You must do that for her.

Start taking your toddler to the dentist for regular checkups by the time he's 3 years old.

Rest and Sleep

■ Naps.

Sometime after your toddler's first birthday, he'll start to give up his morning nap. He no longer needs two naps a day. Unfortunately, he's so active all day long, one nap per day isn't enough, either!

This can be a difficult period. An overtired toddler is a cranky, fussy, whiny toddler. Try to arrange for extra sleep. If your toddler has stopped taking morning naps, put her to bed for her afternoon nap and/or nighttime sleep earlier than usual.

■ Bedtime routine.

Many parents have trouble getting their toddlers to settle down to bed at night. Don't let bedtime become battle time. Try these approaches:

- Have a quiet time with your toddler just before leaving him in his bed for the night. Read a book; sing a song.
- Be sure your toddler has her security blanket, stuffed toy, or pacifier in bed with her.

- Leave a night-light on if your toddler is afraid of the dark.

- Allow a regular bedtime routine—for instance, a book, a song, a sip of water, a hug, a kiss. Do *not* allow your toddler to keep adding steps to the routine. When you get to the last step, say "goodnight" and leave the room.

- What if your toddler keeps calling for you after you leave the room? You can look back into the room every 10 minutes and say "goodnight" again. But do *not* stay in the room. And do *not* allow your toddler to leave the bedroom and rejoin the family, or crawl into your own bed.

- Do comfort your child *immediately* if she wakes up afraid during the night. Prompt comfort means she can get back to sleep quickly.

ACTIVITY

Toddler-Care Choices

Here are some toddler-care situations. Check the action choices you think would be good for each situation. (More than one action choice could be possible for a situation.)

1. Melissa has a busy little toddler, Erik. Melissa's mother buys Erik lots of fancy, expensive clothes that need dry-cleaning. Melissa's mother says these are the best clothes for Erik to wear, and she expects Melissa to use them. What should Melissa do?

   _____ a. Dress Erik in the fancy clothes most of the time to please her mother.

   _____ b. Dress Erik in the fancy clothes whenever her mother will see Erik.

   _____ c. Explain to her mother that Erik needs to wear sturdy, washable clothes most of the time.

   _____ d. Save the fancy clothes for special occasions.

2. Lamar is anxious to toilet-train his toddler, Ebony. Which steps should he take?

   _____ a. Let Ebony sit her doll on the potty chair for a while.

   _____ b. Sit Ebony on the potty chair for five minutes every hour.

   _____ c. Always sit Ebony on the chair right after breakfast when she usually has a bowel movement.

   _____ d. Let Ebony use her own potty chair rather than the adult toilet.

   _____ e. Stop flushing while Ebony's in the bathroom after he notices that Ebony seems scared by the flushing.

(continued)

3. Now that JoAnn's 1½, she won't take a morning nap any more. But she gets cranky without the morning nap. What should JoAnn's caregiver do?

   _____ a. Put JoAnn to bed in the morning as usual, and make her stay there for an hour.

   _____ b. Put JoAnn down for her afternoon nap at 1:00 instead of at her usual 2:00.

   _____ c. Put JoAnn to bed for the night at 6:30 instead of her usual 8:00.

   _____ d. Put JoAnn down for two afternoon naps instead.

4. Enrique, age 2½, always fusses and cries at bedtime. He wants the night-light on. He keeps adding new steps to his bedtime routine. He calls for his parents over and over again after they finally leave his room. What should Enrique's parents do?

   _____ a. Leave the room at the end of the usual bedtime routine, even if Enrique wants more.

   _____ b. Turn off the night-light so the darkness will help Enrique sleep.

   _____ c. Cuddle Enrique for a few minutes on the sofa after he toddles back into the living room.

   _____ d. Say "goodnight" to Enrique again from time to time.

   _____ e. Go to Enrique when he's cried for 10 minutes after he wakes up in the middle of the night.

YOUR TODDLER'S HEALTH

Notice your toddler's symptoms (see pages 6–8). Now that he can talk, he can tell you what's bothering him, too.

Keep up with your toddler's immunizations and well-baby checkups.

ACTIVITY

What immunizations does your toddler need at 15 months?

_____

YOUR TODDLER'S SAFETY

Now that your child can walk, climb, and run, she faces even more dangers! Her safety is your responsibility. You have to keep everything dangerous out of her reach. And you have to supervise her activity at all times. Here are some important toddler safety considerations to keep in mind. Also follow the "Crawling Baby" safety tips on page 23.

Burns and Fire

- Keep handles of pans on the stove turned inward, so your toddler can't reach them.
- Dress your toddler in flame-retardant clothes.
- Keep matches and cigarette lighters out of your toddler's reach.
- Install smoke detectors in your home. Check the batteries each month.
- Have an escape plan in case a fire breaks out in your home. Be sure your toddler knows and can follow the plan.
- Keep space heaters and floor furnaces out of your toddler's reach.
- Set your home hot water heater temperature *below* 130°F.
- Cover unused electric outlets. Tape electric cords to the wall molding or the floor.
- Keep small electric appliances unplugged when they are not being used.

Poisoning

- Keep all household chemicals and cleaners in *locked* cabinets out of your toddler's reach. *Many* household products can poison your toddler if he drinks, breathes, or just touches them.
- Keep all medicines locked up or out of your toddler's reach. Can your toddler open your medicine cabinet? Be sure she's *never* unsupervised in the bathroom.
- Keep your Poison Control Center's number posted near the phone so you can dial it quickly in an emergency.

Falls

- Your toddler loves to climb. Always be alert and remove your toddler from an unsafe, about-to-fall position promptly.

- Watch your toddler on stairs. She needs to practice getting down stairs safely. When you can't watch her, keep stairways blocked off.

- Don't ever leave your toddler unattended in a high chair or shopping cart.

- Lower the crib mattress and raise the crib rails fully to keep your toddler in the crib. Or lower the rails so your toddler can climb out of the crib safely.

Drowning

- *Never* leave a toddler unsupervised around water, even for a moment. A toddler can drown, quickly, in just a few inches of water.

Cars

- Always strap your toddler into a government-approved toddler car seat. (You are required by law to do this in many states.)

- Never move your car in the driveway if your toddler is outside unless the toddler is *in* the car with you or is being *held* by someone else.

- Always stay near your toddler when she is playing in a driveway or near a street.

- Always hold your toddler's hand when you're crossing the street.

ACTIVITY

Toddler-Proofing

A home must be made safe for a crawling baby and toddler. We call this "baby-proofing" (or "toddler-proofing") the home. Practice doing this in two stages.

1. With your classmates, toddler-proof your classroom.

2. Now study your own home. On a separate sheet of paper, make a list of all the things you'd have to do to toddler-proof three rooms (kitchen, bathroom, living room) in your home. Share your list with classmates.

Review of Physical Care, Health, and Safety for Your Toddler

Here are some toddler-care situations. Circle *Yes* or *No* for each one.

1. Your toddler will need a bath at the end of the day. Yes No

2. Although your toddler will brush her teeth herself, you'll have to do the brushing that gets her teeth really clean. Yes No

3. Rough, active play just before bedtime will make your toddler tired and ready for bed. Yes No

4. Your toddler needs to have regular medical checkups even when he's healthy. Yes No

5. Keep your toddler out of the kitchen so she won't get burned. Yes No

6. Your toddler can get hurt by falling out of a shopping cart. Yes No

7. Tell your toddler to go to the side of the driveway when a car is driving in or out. Yes No

8. Your toddler is too young to choose what clothes to wear. Yes No

9. Your toddler is not developing properly if he's not toilet trained by the age of 2½. Yes No

10. Cutting teeth is likely to make your toddler cranky. Yes No

Extra: Tell what is incorrect about each of the statements you circled *No* for.

Physical Care, Health, and Safety for Your Preschool and Kindergarten Child
(Age: 3 years to 5 years)

Through the baby and toddler years, you were wholly responsible for your child's physical care, health, and safety. Your preschool and kindergarten child, though, can do a lot of her own physical care. She can also help to keep herself safe and healthy.

PHYSICAL CARE FOR YOUR YOUNG CHILD

Daily Routine

Your preschool or kindergarten child's daily routine will be like your toddler's daily routine. The difference is that your young child is now skilled enough and mature enough to do things himself.

- He'll dress himself. Give him clothes with elastic waistbands, large zippers, pullover tops.
- He'll enjoy a daily bath. He still needs you to watch him in the bath, though.
- Bedtime routines should be regular and easy by now. He'll probably give up the afternoon nap by the time he's 4 years old.

Tooth Loss

When your child is around 5 years old, she'll start to lose her baby teeth. As each baby tooth comes out, a permanent tooth comes in. She'll also grow more molars.

Your young child needs checkups by a dentist about every six months. She also needs to brush after meals. Avoid sweet snacks. Her permanent teeth are the only ones she'll ever grow from now on!

YOUR YOUNG CHILD'S HEALTH

Your preschool and kindergarten child is exposed to lots of germs because she's out in the world a lot more—at day care or nursery school or kindergarten, at public playgrounds, or on shopping trips.

Immunizations

Be sure to keep up with your young child's immunizations.

ACTIVITY

Which immunizations does your child need at age 4 to 5 years?

_____

Symptoms

Watch for the symptoms listed on pages 6–8.

Chicken Pox

Chicken pox is the most common contagious disease for this age group. Know the signs: multiple small red pimples, then blisters and open sores. If there's an outbreak of chicken pox at your child's day care or preschool, expect your child to catch it. Then she'll be immune for life.

- Keep her from scratching the itchy sores.
- Soothe the itching with a lukewarm baking soda bath. (Dissolve 1 cup of baking soda in a small tubful of water.)
- Your child can go back to school once all the sores are crusted over and no new pox are appearing.

YOUR YOUNG CHILD'S SAFETY

By now, your young child is pretty well able to keep himself safe around your home. (You still need to keep all hazardous substances and medicines locked away.) It's the outside world that presents most dangers to your preschool and kindergarten child.

Traffic

Teach your young child about traffic safety:

- Stop at corners and driveways. Look both ways before crossing.
- *Never* run out into the street between parked cars. Cross the street only at corners.
- Ride a tricycle on the sidewalk, not in the street. Stop riding the tricycle in a driveway if a car starts to move in the drive.
- Always ride in a car with a seat belt fastened.

Molesters

Sadly, you need to teach your preschooler to be careful of strangers. Tell him *never* to accept a ride from a stranger. If a stranger wants to take him for a ride, or take him away anyplace, he should *run* away, quickly.

You must also teach your young child about "bad touching." Sexual abuse of young children is far too common today. Keep the warnings low-key and friendly. Simply tell your young child that she doesn't have to let anyone (even someone she knows; even a relative) touch her private body areas. Tell her to tell you if anyone does try to touch her in those areas.

Review of Physical Care, Health, and Safety for Your Preschool and Kindergarten Child

Here are some statements about physical care, health, and safety for your young child. Circle *Yes* or *No* for each.

1. Your preschool child will cut four final "baby" teeth. Yes No

2. Your young child needs final DTP and polio immunizations. Yes No

3. Your young child can learn to cross the street on her own. Yes No

4. Your preschool or kindergarten child is too young to to understand about "bad touching." Yes No

5. Your young child can handle clothes with large zippers. Yes No

6. You should try to protect your young child from getting chicken pox. Yes No

7. Expect your kindergarten child to need an afternoon nap. Yes No

8. Your young child should have his first visit to the dentist when he's 6 years old. Yes No

Extra: Tell what is incorrect about each of the statements you circled *No* for.

```
┌─────────────────────────────────┐
│              II                 │
│                                 │
│         NUTRITION               │
│                                 │
└─────────────────────────────────┘
```

WHAT IS NUTRITION?

Nutrition depends upon what you and your child eat. It's in the cereal you had for breakfast, and in the banana your child ate as a snack.

Nutrition is inherent in the process of eating. It's in your child's breakfast, lunch, dinner, and snacks.

WHAT ARE NUTRIENTS?

Nutrients are substances in food. They're what nutrition is all about. Your child's body uses nutrients it gets from food to keep him alive, healthy, and growing.

WHAT DO NUTRIENTS DO FOR YOUR CHILD'S BODY?

Here are the important things nutrients give to your child's body.

■ **Energy.**

Nutrients from food give *energy* to your child's body.

■ **Growth.**

Your child's body uses nutrients from food to *grow*, and to *repair* worn-out parts.

■ **Health.**

Nutrients from food help your child's body fight off illness and stay *healthy*.

■ Functioning.

Your child's body uses food nutrients to keep its different parts *running*.

WHAT YOUR CHILD NEEDS TO GET FROM FOOD

Think of your child's body as a house that's being built. Lots of different materials go into a house to make it complete. Like a house, your child's body needs lots of different materials—food nutrients—while it's being built.

Your child's body is like a machine that is running all the time, too. Any machine needs fuel to run on. Food is the fuel that keeps your child's body running and in good repair.

To grow, stay healthy, and keep running, your child's body needs seven important nutrients.

1. protein
2. minerals
3. vitamins
4. carbohydrates (sugar & starch)

5. water
6. fiber
7. fat

Let's see what each of these does and what foods you'll find them in.

Nutrition Chart

Nutrient	What It Does	Foods That Have a Lot of This Nutrient
Protein	Builds cells, muscles. Repairs worn-out cells. Gives energy.	Meat, fish, poultry. Eggs, milk. Dried beans & peas. Nuts, some cereals.
Minerals (2 most important)		
Calcium	Makes teeth & bones strong & hard.	Milk, things made from milk (cheese, yogurt). Leafy green vegetables.
Iron	Builds blood. Helps blood carry oxygen to cells.	Eggs, liver, low-fat meats. Whole grains, dried beans. Green leafy vegetables.
Vitamins (4 most important)		
Vitamin A	Helps eyesight. Keeps skin, nose, throat healthy.	Eggs. Green vegetables. Yellow vegetables.
Vitamin B complex (a group)	Helps body get energy from food. Keeps nerves healthy. Helps make blood.	Meat. Milk. Eggs. Whole grains.
Vitamin C	Keeps gums, teeth, bones healthy. Helps body cells work right.	Citrus fruits (like oranges & grapefruit). Tomatoes, potatoes. Dark green vegetables.
Vitamin D	Lets body use calcium & phosphorus to build strong teeth & bones.	Milk with vitamin D added. (Nonfood sources: Sunlight on skin. Vitamin D drops.)
Carbohydrates		
Sugars	Give quick energy.	Table sugar (sucrose). Milk (lactose). Fruit (fructose).

(continued)

Nutrition Chart *(continued)*

NUTRIENT	WHAT IT DOES	FOODS THAT HAVE A LOT OF THIS NUTRIENT
Starches	Give long-lasting energy. Supply fiber, minerals, vitamins.	Cereals, bread, pasta. Dried beans & peas. Rice. Root vegetables (like potatoes).
Fat	Is a super-concentrated energy source (you need only a little).	Butter, oil, margarine, salad dressing. Nuts, eggs, milk, cheese.
Water	Helps digest foods. Makes muscles work. Keeps body temperature where it should be.	Liquids (milk, juice, water). Many foods (e.g., a potato is 75% water).

ACTIVITY

Nutrition Knowledge Check

Use the information in the nutrition chart to answer these questions.

1. Which of these foods gives your child a good serving of protein?

   hamburger   fruit juice   baked beans
   apple   scrambled egg   birthday cake
   potato chips   milk   tuna fish

2. Suppose your child won't drink much milk. How can she get the calcium she needs to build strong teeth and bones?

3. If your child didn't eat fruits and vegetables, what health problems do you think he might have?

4. What vitamin is called the "sunshine vitamin"? Why did it get this nickname?

5. Which of these foods gives your child a good serving of *natural* sugar (not table sugar)? Circle them. Which of these foods will give your child a serving of starch? Underline them.

   cookies   spaghetti   watermelon
   peach   lemonade   oatmeal
   toast   skim milk   baked potato

(continued)

6. Fiber has been in the news a lot in the past few years. Do you know why? (Hint: It has something to do with a well-known disease.)

FOOD "TRAPS" YOU SHOULD WATCH OUT FOR

Too Much Fat

Your child (and you!) only needs one tablespoon of fat every day. Any more fat than that piles up in the body. Your child becomes overweight, which can shorten his life. Fats can also clog blood vessels, which causes heart disease and strokes.

Most foods do contain some fat. So it's easy for your child to get too much fat with his food. To be sure your child eats only a little fat, be sure he eats only a few high-fat foods—like butter and fried foods.

Too Much Sugar

Sugar does give your child quick energy. But it doesn't give her anything else.

Sugar is habit-forming. A child quickly develops a taste for sugar, and wants more and more of it. At the same time, she'll eat less and less of the foods with lots of nutrients.

Also, sugary foods are often high-fat foods—like cakes and chocolate. If your child eats lots of high-sugar, high-fat foods, she'll tend to get overweight and could develop heart disease when she gets older.

Sugar sticks to the teeth, too, and makes teeth decay.

Too Much Sodium (Salt)

Lots of foods are very salty—like bacon and most potato chips. Does your child get a lot of salt in his diet? Then he may develop high blood pressure, which can lead to heart disease and stroke.

Most foods contain some salt, or sodium. It's easy to get too much. So try to be sure your child eats mostly unsalted, low-sodium foods.

Processed Foods

A "processed" food has been changed from its original, natural state. White bread and instant mashed potatoes are examples of processed foods.

Processed foods are often low in nutrients. You can count on them to have less fiber and less food value than the original, unprocessed food.

Try to be sure your child gets a good variety of original, unrefined foods—like brown rice, wheat bread, and *real* potatoes. When your child eats these foods, she's getting the fiber, vitamins, and minerals she needs.

ACTIVITY

Food Trap Knowledge Check

1. Some of these foods are high in fat. Draw a line through each of the high-fat foods.

butter	margarine	nuts
french fries	ice cream	lima beans
yogurt	mayonnaise	chocolate

2. Read the lists of ingredients on food labels. How many different words for sugar can you find? Write them here. (Hint: Many of the other words for sugar end in the letters *ose*).

   _____   _____

   _____   _____

   _____   _____

3. What word on a food label's list of ingredients tells you the food contains extra salt?

4. Some of these foods have a lot of sodium, or salt. Draw a line through each of the high-salt foods.

bacon	milk	popcorn
canned soup	potato chips	banana
fruit juice	soy sauce	ham

5. What does "enriched" mean on a loaf of white bread? Why has the bread been "enriched"?

6. Read a variety of ingredient lists from jars and boxes of food. On a separate sheet of paper, write the names of ingredients you don't recognize, can't pronounce, or wonder about. Share these lists in class. What's the strangest-sounding ingredient anyone came up with? What actually is each of these ingredients? Why is it in the food?

CHOOSING FOODS: THE FOOD GROUPS

Now you know what the important nutrients are: protein, minerals, vitamins, carbohydrates (sugars and starches), fat, water, and fiber.

Your job as a parent or caregiver is to be sure your child gets the right amount of these important nutrients almost every day. How do you do this? Do you have to figure out the amounts of, say, vitamin C, iron, and fiber in every thing your child eats? How could you do that?!

Thank goodness, there's an easy way. You just have to be sure your child eats several servings from each of four food groups each day. (You'll find the amounts in the section later in this booklet for each age group.)

These are the food groups:

1. *Milk*—and foods made from milk, like yogurt, cheese, cottage cheese, and ice milk. (Choose low-fat products.)

2. *Meat*—and other foods that are high in *protein*, like:
   Meats: chicken, turkey, fish, lean beef, lamb, pork.
   Other protein foods: dry beans, dry peas, nuts.

3. *Vegetables & Fruits* (Fresh are best; serve some raw.)
   Yellow vegetables include winter squash, carrots, sweet potatoes.
   Green vegetables include broccoli, green beans, collards, spinach.
   Citrus fruits include oranges, grapefruit, lemons, limes, tangerines.
   Other fruits include apples, cherries, plums, peaches, melons, berries.

4. *Bread & Cereal*—also grains and pasta.
   Includes bread, cooked and dry cereal, oatmeal, noodles, pasta, rice, corn grits, macaroni.

GUIDELINES FOR A GOOD DIET

Does all this seem like too much? Here's a simple set of guidelines you can follow to be sure your child's diet is healthy.

1. Eat a variety of foods.

2. Eat a low amount of fat, especially animal fat.

3. Eat enough starch and fiber, especially fresh fruits and fresh vegetables.

4. Eat a low amount of sugar, and foods with sugar in them.

5. Eat a low amount of sodium (salty-tasting foods).

ACTIVITY

A Sample Day's Diet

Do you think you could make up a well-balanced diet for one day's meals? You want a balance of foods from the four groups. Write your day's meals here.

Breakfast	*Lunch*	*Dinner*
_____	_____	_____
_____	_____	_____
_____	_____	_____

Snacks

_____   _____

_____   _____

_____   _____

Do your day's meals supply all the needed nutrients? After each nutrient listed here, write the foods from your menu that have a good amount of that nutrient.

Protein: _____

Minerals: _____

Vitamins: _____

Carbohydrates

  Sugar: _____

  Starch: _____

Water: _____

Fiber: _____

Fat (be sure your foods don't have too much of this): _____

Do you need to make any changes to your meal plan to make it better balanced?

You know that your child needs certain nutrients to grow and stay healthy. You know which foods can give your child those nutrients. Now let's look at just how you can use what you know to make sure your child has a good diet at three different age levels.

Feeding Your Baby
(Age: Birth to 1 year)

Feeding a young baby is really quite simple. Up to the age of about six months, all your baby needs for food is milk. Milk is a complete food for your baby. It gives her protein, fat, sugar, vitamins, and minerals.

You have two ways to give your baby the milk she needs: breast-feeding and/or bottle-feeding.

BREAST AND BOTTLE FEEDING

Breast Milk: Nature's Perfect Infant Food

Breast milk is the ideal food for a baby. It's easy to digest. It's designed to give a baby all the nutrients babies need.

As soon as a baby is born, the mother's breasts are ready to nurse the infant. The first few days after birth, the mother's breasts produce a liquid called *colostrum* instead of real milk. Colostrum gives the baby important *antibodies*—substances that will protect the baby from many illnesses and allergies.

A few days after birth, the mother's breasts begin to produce milk. It's a great system: The more the baby nurses, the more milk the mother's breasts produce.

The nutrients the baby gets from breast milk come from the food the baby's mother eats. So a mother who's breast-feeding needs to eat a well-balanced diet. She needs to eat plenty of foods from all four food groups. She also needs to drink lots of milk, juice, and water.

Bottle Feeding

You can feed a baby the milk he needs from a bottle. You feed a baby *formula*, not plain cow's milk. Cow's milk is fine for baby cows, but not for baby people. Formula is a mixture of cow's milk, water, and sugar. Formula is more like breast milk than cow's milk is.

You can buy formula that's already prepared, in cans or bottles. (Once you've opened prepared formula, you must keep it in the refrigerator.) You can also buy concentrated or powdered formula that you prepare yourself according to directions on the package. Or you can prepare your own formula, using evaporated or powdered milk.

Prepared formula is most expensive to buy. Making your own formula is the cheapest choice.

Germs grow very easily in milk. So when you bottle-feed, you must be sure to keep your baby's bottles and nipples very clean. Bottles, bottle caps, and mixing equipment get safely clean in a dishwasher. Nipples you need to wash carefully by hand.

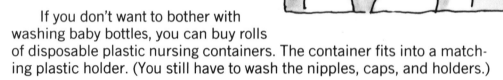

If you don't want to bother with washing baby bottles, you can buy rolls of disposable plastic nursing containers. The container fits into a matching plastic holder. (You still have to wash the nipples, caps, and holders.)

Your doctor may want your bottle-fed baby to take vitamin drops.

Advantages of Breast Feeding

- Easy to digest; won't cause stomach upsets.
- Gives baby immunity to some diseases.
- Establishes especially close bond between mother and baby.
- Helps mother regain her pre-pregnancy figure.
- Saves time: nothing to prepare, wash, warm up.
- Convenient: baby's meal is always ready, any place, any time.
- Cheap: no formula to buy.
- Satisfies baby's sucking instinct.
- Night feedings are very easy.

Advantages of Bottle Feeding

- You know exactly how much baby is taking.
- Always have enough milk: supply doesn't depend on mother's well-being.
- Mother is free to eat the way she wants to.

- Baby can be fed anywhere without embarrassment.
- Gives father equal chance to be close to baby.

ACTIVITY

Breast and Bottle Feeding Review

Here are some statements about breast and bottle feeding. Write True or False next to each one.

_____ 1. A mother with a job outside the home can't breast-feed her baby.

_____ 2. A newborn baby may need to be fed as often as every two hours.

_____ 3. If your baby is being breast-fed, you can't give her any bottle feedings.

_____ 4. If a mother breast-feeds her baby too often, her milk supply will run out.

_____ 5. Breast-fed babies are likely to have fewer illnesses than bottle-fed babies.

_____ 6. A bottle-fed baby does not need to be held while he's being fed.

_____ 7. A baby's formula is made of cow's milk, water, and sugar.

_____ 8. A mother who does not like breast-feeding should not force herself to breast-feed her baby.

_____ 9. A breast-feeding mother can eat anything she likes.

_____ 10. Bottle-fed babies don't bond closely with their parents.

Question. Some fathers feel left out when the mother breast-feeds their baby. What can these parents do to make the father feel included in the feeding process?

HOW OFTEN DO YOU FEED?
HOW MUCH DO YOU FEED?

Your baby will "tell" you how often and much to feed her. How? She'll cry when she's hungry. She'll suck at the breast or bottle until she's had enough. Then she'll stop. If she hasn't had enough, she'll cry for more. When she's hungry again, ready for her next feeding, she'll start crying again.

Trust these messages from your baby. When you respond to her cries of hunger, you're making her feel secure. She's learning to trust the world around her. Don't urge the baby to take more milk than she wants, either. If you try to force food on your baby, she'll start to think of mealtime as a struggle. She'll stop feeding easily and happily.

Your baby will actually *lose* weight right after birth. When he's about ten days old, he'll be back up to his birth weight. From then on, he'll gain *about* 6 or 8 ounces each week. As long as you're feeding your baby the amounts of milk he "asks" for each time he's hungry, he'll be getting enough.

Many new parents and caregivers worry about getting a baby on a regular schedule of feeding. If you feed your baby whenever he seems to be hungry, will this teach him to want food often? No. A young baby wakes up from hunger, not from habit. As the baby gets older, his stomach will be able to go longer between feedings. Most babies settle into an every-4-hours (or so) feeding schedule by the time they weigh 7 or 8 pounds.

What about middle-of-the-night feedings? Your baby will probably sleep through that 2 a.m. feeding by the time she's a month or two old.

ACTIVITY

Feeding Decisions

Read each description. Then decide whether the baby is getting enough to eat.

1. Baby Sean takes a full 8-ounce bottle at his first feeding, then drops down to 6-ounce bottles for his next three feedings, then finishes with an 8-ounce feeding. Sean seems satisfied with each feeding and doesn't fuss much during the four hours between feedings. Sean's mother worries that the baby should be taking 8 ounces at each feeding.

   Is this baby getting enough to eat? Yes _____ No _____

2. Baby Yolanda takes 3 ounces of milk at her first feeding, instead of the usual 6 ounces she has at other feedings. To make up for the small breakfast, Yolanda's mother offers the baby 3 extra ounces of milk at lunchtime. But Yolanda can't take 3 extra ounces after her usual 6-ounce lunch, even though she's been fussing from hunger since mid-morning.

   Is this baby getting enough to eat? Yes _____ No _____

3. Baby Harry gains about 3 ounces in weight each week. Baby William gains about 6 ounces in weight each week. The babies'

(continued)

grandmother tells Harry's parents that their baby must be underfed. Is Harry getting enough to eat? Yes _____ No _____

Feeding Guidelines

How would you decide if your baby was getting enough to eat? Think of two good guidelines.

1. _____

2. _____

SOLID FOOD

Adding Solid Food

When do you start adding "solid" food to your baby's all-milk diet? Usually, when your baby is 4 to 6 months old.

These "solids" aren't very solid at first. They're strained and thinned food, with no lumps—for example, oatmeal thinned with milk, or strained, almost-liquid peaches.

You can't feed your baby real solid foods, like pieces of hot dog. She can't chew yet, and she doesn't know how to swallow chunks. She could easily choke.

You offer strained and thinned solids so your baby starts to get used to new and different foods. And by the time your baby is about 6 months old, he needs extra nutrients beyond what he gets in his milk.

Here are some tips for starting to add solids to your baby's diet:

- Add only *one* new food at a time.
- Give very small amounts of solids at first.
- Keep baby's milk intake high.
- Let baby decide which solids she likes and which ones she doesn't want.
- Don't mix solid foods.
- Offer a variety of solid foods (but only one at a time).
- Feed solids *without* added sugar or salt.

What Solid Foods Do You Feed Your Baby?

Cereal is often a baby's first solid food. (This is special, precooked *baby* cereal that you mix with milk or formula.) Some babies prefer *strained fruit*. Once your baby is eating cereal and fruit, you can offer *strained vegetables*. By the time your baby is about 9 months old, you can introduce lumpy or chunky food.

Finger foods are fun for 6- to 12-month-old babies. These are foods your baby can pick up and "chew" on, making eating fun and easy. (Your toothless baby chews with tongue and gums.) Finger foods are your baby's first step toward feeding herself. Here are some sample finger foods for your baby:

- toast sticks or crusts
- crackers (like zweiback)
- banana pieces
- cooked carrot pieces
- apple, orange, or pear slices (peeled, core & seeds removed)

ACTIVITY

Solid Food Feeding Choices

These parents are starting to feed their babies solid food. Are they following the solid-feeding tips? Decide Yes or No for each.

1. Sue and Bob start Baby Paul on solid food by giving him strained pears the first day, oatmeal cereal the second day, strained beets the third day, and mashed hamburger the fourth day.

   Yes   No

2. Miguel knows mashed banana is very nutritious. He keeps feeding banana to Baby Bianca even though she doesn't seem to like it.

   Yes   No

3. Maura has started adding cereal and strained fruit to Baby Christian's diet. She is giving Christian almost as much milk as he had before he started eating solid foods.

   Yes   No

4. This week, Janessa started feeding Baby Julius cereal mixed with milk. Next week, Janessa plans to add strained applesauce to the baby's diet.

   Yes   No

(continued)

5. George has tasted Baby Nathaniel's strained baby food. It's so plain-tasting! George plans to add some sugar to the strained fruit, and some salt to the beans, so Nathaniel will like the taste of the food better.

Yes   No

Finger Foods to Avoid

Some finger foods aren't safe because your baby can choke on them. List some foods here that you think could be a choking danger. Share your list with classmates.

_____   _____

_____   _____

_____   _____

_____   _____

BABY FOODS: HOMEMADE AND STORE-BOUGHT

When you add solids to your baby's diet, you can buy ready-made baby food in jars. You can also make your own baby food at home.

Store-Bought Baby Food

When you buy ready-made baby food, keep these points in mind:

- Read the labels. Buy only baby food with *no* sugar and *no* salt and *no* preservatives added.
- Buy plain fruit, plain vegetables, and plain meat.
- *Don't* buy "dinners" or mixtures of meats, vegetables, or fruits with starches.
- Give fruits for dessert. Avoid puddings and gelatins.

Homemade Baby Food

It's easy to make your own baby food from the foods your family eats. Here's how:

- Put cooked vegetables and fruit through a grinder, blender, or food processor.
- Mash up cooked food with a fork.
- Chop up cooked meats very finely.
- Make foods moist if needed by adding milk, water, or broth.
- Give "finger foods" your baby can pick up and feed to herself.
- Keep salt and sugar out of your baby's food.
- Avoid hot or spicy foods for your baby.

ACTIVITY

Baby Food Labels

Read the ingredient lists and labels on baby food jars at a grocery store. Write here what you find for five different kinds of baby food.

1. Fruit:
2. Vegetable:
3. Meat:
4. Mixed dinner:
5. Pudding:

Baby Food Recipes

Find some simple baby food recipes. Try them out. Taste them. Feed them to a baby. Share your recipes with classmates.

STARTING TO USE A CUP

You can start to offer your baby small sips of milk from a cup when he's 5 or 6 months old. He won't get much at first, but that's okay. Bit by bit, he'll master cup-drinking. By about 12 months, he'll be getting most or all of his daily milk from the cup instead of a bottle or breast.

You'll probably want to buy a baby cup with handles and plastic top to start. The handles let your baby use the cup by himself, which is what he'll want to do. The top has a spout for your baby to sip from. And with the top on, when your baby dumps, tosses, or drops the cup, the milk won't all spill out.

STEPS TO HAPPY MEALTIME

- Relax and enjoy mealtime. He wants food; you want him to have food. You're on the same team!

- Let baby take his time. Don't try to rush him. (It won't work.)

- Let baby decide how much she wants to eat. She knows what's best for her.

- Expect a mess. Your baby will plunge into her solid foods with her hands before she learns to use a spoon. This is how she learns to enjoy her meals, and how she learns to feed herself.

- Expect changes. Sometimes your baby will want more to eat, sometimes less. Go along with what she wants .

Baby Feeding Review

Here are some statements about feeding a baby. Circle *Yes* or *No* for each one.

1. The more a baby nurses, the more milk the mother's breasts produce.   Yes   No

2. Mixed store-bought dinners of meat and starches are very nutritious.   Yes   No

3. Finger foods are usually a baby's first solid food.   Yes   No

4. Baby bottles, caps, and nipples must be carefully washed.   Yes   No

5. Your baby's bottle is filled with low-fat cow's milk.   Yes   No

6. It's best to feed your baby whenever she's hungry, not on a schedule you think is best.   Yes   No

7. Your baby should gain weight steadily.   Yes   No

8. You need to add solid food to your baby's diet by the time he's 10 months old.   Yes   No

9. Teach your baby to eat solids with a spoon, not with his fingers.   Yes   No

10. Your baby will get most of his milk from a cup by the time he's 1 year old.   Yes   No

Extra: Tell what is incorrect about each of the statements you circled *No* for.

Feeding Your Toddler
(Age: 1 year to 3 years)

HOW MUCH DO YOU FEED YOUR TODDLER?

Your toddler is the most amazingly active bundle of energy you've ever seen. He's crawling, running, climbing—on the go all the time. So you'd think this nonstop high-speed machine would gobble great amounts of food to fuel his ever-active body. Not so.

A toddler doesn't stay interested in anything for very long, including meals. Your toddler sits down to eat, and a few minutes later he wants to explore something else.

Also, a toddler grows more slowly than a baby. So a toddler's appetite doesn't grow as quickly as a baby's appetite does.

Relax. Offer your toddler a variety of nutritious foods, when he wants to eat. Let him eat only as much as he wants. Try to be sure your toddler eats these amounts almost every day:

- Milk (or foods made from milk)—three servings.
- Meat, chicken, turkey, or fish—two servings. (Or other protein food.)
- Fruits & vegetables—four servings, some raw.
- Bread or cereal—whole grain, three servings. (A "serving" for a toddler is small: 2 tablespoons of meat, fruit or vegetable; 1/2 cup milk or milk product; 1/2 slice bread; 1/4 cup pasta, rice, or cereal.)

ACTIVITY

A Toddler Menu

In the space below, write out a sample day's food for a toddler. Include amounts of each food. Be sure your toddler gets a well-balanced mix of foods!

Breakfast: _____

Lunch: _____

(continued)

Dinner: _____

Snacks: _____

A Real-Life Toddler

Observe a toddler for a day. Record what the child eats during the day. Separate your list into the four food groups.

Milk: _____

Meat (Protein): _____

Fruits & Vegetables: _____

Bread & Cereal: _____

1. Has your toddler eaten a balanced diet today? _____
2. Has your toddler gotten enough of the nutrients he or she needs? _____
3. If your answer to 1 or 2 is no, explain what is missing in the diet.

_____

_____

MEALTIME OR BATTLE TIME?

Feeding problems are most likely to develop during your child's toddler years. Why? Because of the *parent's* attitude.

A toddler doesn't stay interested in food for very long. A toddler doesn't need a large amount of food, just a *variety* of foods. A toddler plays with food; a lot of it doesn't get eaten. And a toddler is in the "no" stage: Ask your toddler a direct question ("Do you want some potato?") and she'll usually say "no."

This perfectly normal toddler behavior upsets parents. A parent who's paid for food and prepared it feels angry, frustrated, and even rejected when the child refuses to eat the food. The parent hates to see food wasted and thinks it's wrong. The parent worries about being a bad parent if she can't get her child to eat a lot.

Use these hints to avoid feeding problems with your toddler:

▪ Your child will not starve himself.

Your child will eat what he needs if the food is available.

▪ Let your child feed himself.

Make his meals reasonably easy to feed to himself. Help only as much as he wants you to.

▪ Accept the mess.

A toddler is learning to get food into her mouth, using her hands as well as a spoon. While she's learning, the food goes everywhere—all over her face, in her hair, on her clothes, on the floor.

▪ Let your child eat the way she wants.

Let her eat the food in any order she wants. Let her combine any foods in any way she wants. Let her use hands, or pieces of toast, or green beans, instead of a spoon.

▪ Let your child decide how much to eat.

Don't urge your child to eat "just one more bite." Don't say "eat this for Daddy." Don't tell your child he has to "clean his plate." The more you say these things, the more you'll turn your child against food.

▪ Keep mealtime relaxed and enjoyable.

Sit with your child while he's eating. Let him end the meal when he gets restless.

▪ Accept variations.

Some days (or weeks) your child will not be very hungry. Other days (or weeks) he'll go on an eating jag. This is normal.

■ **Offer nutritious snacks.**

Or try five or six small meals instead of three big ones.

■ **Don't use food as a bribe or reward.**

Don't hold food back for punishment. Keep food separate from discipline.

If you keep your emotions out of your child's feeding, you'll avoid most feeding problems!

ACTIVITY

What Would You Do?

Here are some toddler feeding situations. Decide what you would do for each one.

1. One-year-old Mikey insists on feeding himself. Most of the food goes on the floor or on Mikey's feeding tray. Mikey's parents are sure he's not getting enough to eat.

   What would you do?

2. Two-year-old Tanisha doesn't stay interested in anything for very long. She only sits still for a meal for five minutes, then loses interest in eating. Tanisha can't get enough to eat at breakfast, lunch, and dinner when she only spends five minutes at each meal.

   What would you do?

3. For the past three months Yvette, age 2, has been eating a bowl of cereal for breakfast and a sandwich and piece of fruit for lunch. Suddenly she's only eating half a bowl of cereal and half a sandwich.

   What would you do?

SWEETS AND SNACKS

Toddlers love to snack. Does your child eat three main meals a day? Then she's almost sure to need a mid-morning snack and a mid-afternoon snack. A hungry toddler is a grumpy toddler.

But beware! Don't fall into the trap of thinking that snacks must be sweet and sugary. Instead, think of snacks as extra helpings of your toddler's daily diet—like whole-wheat crackers, fresh fruit slices, celery and cream cheese.

Young children don't *naturally* want soft drinks, candy, and dough-nuts. If you don't have these foods around, your child won't miss them. If you *do* offer sugary, high-fat foods for snacks, you could start your child on a lifelong habit of eating these foods. That habit could fill your child's teeth with cavities and lead your child to obesity and heart disease when he's an adult—or even a teenager!

ACTIVITY

Choosing Healthy Snacks

Here's a list of foods a toddler could eat for a snack. Circle the snacks that would be a good food choice for a toddler.

popcorn	doughnut	crackers
cookie	fruit juice	peanut butter
banana	potato chips	soda
peanuts	ice cream	cheese

Extra. Can you tell why the uncircled snacks are not good food choices?

FUN FOOD IDEAS

Try these ideas to perk up a fussy toddler's interest in food:

• Serve spiral, alphabet, or dinosaur pasta, or colored pasta.

- Cut bread or sandwiches into fun shapes with cookie cutters.
- Offer frozen green peas right from the freezer bag.
- Cut fruits and vegetables into rings.
- Stick half an apple or pear (cored, peeled) onto a popsicle stick.
- Freeze fruit juices (l00% fruit, no sugar) into popsicles.
- Serve raw vegetables with yogurt dip.
- Make faces on food with berries or raisins.
- Serve "lunch" or "supper" foods for breakfast.
- Serve a meal of tiny servings of finger foods in an ice-cube tray, a different item in each cube compartment.
- Let your toddler help in the kitchen. He can stir, pour ingredients you've already measured out, taste the casserole.

Toddler Feeding Review

Here are some statements about feeding toddlers. Circle *Yes* or *No* for each one.

1. Your toddler's appetite grows more slowly than your baby's appetite does.   Yes   No

2. A lot of toddler feeding problems are caused by the parents' attitudes.   Yes   No

3. Your toddler won't eat enough if you let him decide how much to eat.   Yes   No

4. Your toddler will want and need to snack between meals.   Yes   No

5. Making good foods fun to eat will make your toddler want to eat fun but junky foods.   Yes   No

6. Promise your toddler a nice dessert if he'll eat his vegetables.   Yes   No

7. Toddlers naturally want sweet foods.   Yes   No

8. Your toddler can help you when you're getting meals ready.   Yes   No

9. Your toddler is so messy when she eats! Start teaching her table manners now.   Yes   No

10. Your toddler can eat five or six small meals a day instead of three main meals.   Yes   No

Extra: Tell what is incorrect about each of the statements you circled *No* for.

Feeding Your Preschool and Kindergarten Child (Age: 3 years to 5 years)

HOW MUCH AND WHAT DO YOU FEED YOUR YOUNG CHILD?

Feeding your preschool and kindergarten child is a lot like feeding your toddler. Follow the guidelines for a toddler's daily diet:

- Milk group—three servings.
- Meat group—two servings.
- Fruits & Vegetables—four servings.
- Bread & Cereal—three servings.

The only difference is that the servings for your preschool and kindergarten child would be larger than the portion you'd give your toddler.

As you do with a toddler, offer your preschool or kindergarten child nutritious snacks between meals. Expect variations in your young child's appetite from day to day and week to week. Avoid feeding battles by following the "Mealtime or Battle Time?" guidelines in the section you just read about toddlers.

Here's what most preschool and kindergarten children like for food:

- Bright colors.
- Small helpings.
- Each food separately (not in casseroles).
- Mild flavors.
- Mild temperatures (*not* hot).
- Different textures (some soft, some crisp, some in between).
- Desserts.
- Anything they've helped to make.

Different kids, of course, will have different tastes.

ACTIVITY

Food Choices

Which of these foods would you expect your preschool or kinder-garten child to like? Circle them.

turnips	creamed tuna	carrots
spicy salsa	broccoli	banana bread
oranges	steaming hot soup	

chicken, rice, and bean casserole

1 helping each of raw green beans, mashed potato, and hamburger

MEALTIMES

Your toddler couldn't sit still long enough to join you for a family meal. He might start the meal with you, but he'd scurry away long before anyone else was finished.

Your 3- or 4-year-old is ready to join the rest of the family at the dinner table. Family mealtime can be a great learning experience for your preschool or kindergarten child:

■ Social time.

Family mealtime is a wonderful time for togetherness. Everybody in the family tells each other about their day—what they're concerned about, what's happening to them. At family mealtime, your young child learns how to share his daily life experiences with other family members. He also learns how to make mealtimes a cheerful, pleasant social event.

■ Food-learning time.

Family mealtime is a terrific time to introduce your young child to new foods. She'll be much more willing to try a food that other family members are eating. (But let her decide what to try, and how much.)

■ Table manners.

At the family meal table, your young child will learn simple table man-ners—saying "please" and "thank you," setting the table, asking nicely, passing things around, using a fork instead of fingers, asking to be excused, helping to clean up.

Mealtime Behavior

Here are some ways of behaving at a family meal. Which of them would be normal and acceptable dinner-table behavior for a 3- or 4-year-old child? Check the column for OK or Not OK.

	OK	Not OK
1. Spills a little milk out of cup.	—	—
2. Spits mashed potatoes onto floor.	—	—
3. Talks excitedly about what happened at day care today.	—	—
4. Refuses to eat any beet greens.	—	—
5. Turns cup of milk upside down onto table.	—	—
6. Won't help take used plates to sink.	—	—
7. Argues with younger brother.	—	—
8. Takes tiny servings of new foods but refuses larger helpings.	—	—
9. Helps set table.	—	—
10. Leaves table a number of times during meal.	—	—

HELPING IN THE KITCHEN

Your preschool or kindergarten child will love to help out in the kitchen. He's more capable of being a really useful helper now than when he was a toddler. He can set the table, wash and peel vegetables and fruits, make salads, break eggs into a bowl, mix things up in a blender.

While your young child is helping in the kitchen is the perfect time to start teaching him about nutrition, about what's valuable in different foods. You can tell him, for instance, "This milk will make your bones and teeth strong." Or you can say, "This bread will give you energy so you can run fast."

Your young child will also be very interested in *where* food comes from. She'll enjoy short trips to an orchard, or a farm. She'll also have fun growing her own food, especially fast-growing plants like lettuce, spinach, and radishes.

`ACTIVITY`

Helping: Yes or No?

Your young child can't do everything in the kitchen, of course. Write at least five or six things your young child *can* safely do to help in the kitchen. Then write at least five or six things your young child *can't* safely do to help in the kitchen.

Things Your Young Child
CAN Do to Help in Kitchen

Things Your Young Child
CAN'T Do to Help in Kitchen

_____   _____

_____   _____

_____   _____

_____   _____

_____   _____

_____   _____

_____   _____

_____   _____

FOOD AWAY FROM HOME

You can pretty much control what food is available to your baby and toddler. But your preschooler, and especially your kindergartner, will spend time with other children. Your young child can see what other kids are eating. If they're getting lots of sweets and fried foods and he isn't, you may face a problem. He'll want to eat what the other kids are eating. What do you do?

First, don't keep sweets or "junk" foods in your home. When your child asks for an unhealthy snack, say you don't have any. Then offer him a healthy substitute, like banana or cheese or crackers.

Next, don't overreact if your child eats some of her friend's candy, or a piece of chocolate cake at a birthday party. Having sweets once in a while isn't a problem. What you want to avoid is a steady diet of sweets (or fried food, or other unhealthy foods).

You can also agree to buy your child a small amount of some sweet treat (or cheese doodads) at some regular time. If your child knows he will have some treat when you go shopping on Saturday morning, he'll be more willing to accept it when you say no, you won't buy any candy right now.

If your child has grown up on a nonsweet, nutritious diet, she probably won't want to stuff herself with junk foods once she gets to school and can choose for herself.

ACTIVITY

What to Do?

You don't want your young child to eat sweets and foods with little nutritional value. So what would you do in each of these situations?

1. Your preschool child is invited to a birthday party. You know he'll be served cake and ice cream. What do you do?

2. Your kindergarten child's classmates bring sweet treats to school for snack time. Your child wants sweet snacks, too, not the apple you usually send to school with her. What do you do?

3. Your young child loves to shop for himself at the penny-candy counter. What do you do?

OVERWEIGHT KIDS

Fatness in young children is a problem in the United States today. Our average American diet, rich in fatty foods and sweets, produces overweight children. Overweight kids tend to grow into overweight adults, with extra risks for heart disease and stroke.

What should you do if your child is obviously overweight? First, check with your doctor or health-care worker to decide if your child does in fact have a weight problem. Then change your child's eating habits to slow down her weight gain so she'll thin out as she gets taller. You *do not* put a young child on a weight-loss diet.

Here are some things you can do to help your young child get slimmer:

• Cut out rich desserts. Offer fresh fruit instead.

- Bake or broil foods instead of frying them.
- Use low-fat spreads on bread—low-fat cream cheese, for example, instead of butter.
- Make sure your child gets a lot of exercise.
- Stay away from high-fat fast-food restaurants.
- Serve pure fruit juice with seltzer instead of fizzy soft drinks.
- Set a good example. It's best if no one in the home is eating foods that your overweight child isn't supposed to eat.

ACTIVITY

Slimming Down—True or False?

Here are some statements about helping an overweight young child slim down. Write True or False in the blank next to each statement.

_____ 1. Give your child a bowl of fruit instead of the cake the rest of the family is eating.

_____ 2. Dance and tumble around with your child every day.

_____ 3. Feed your child more vegetables and fruits and fewer starches and fats.

_____ 4. Offer a small sweet dessert as a treat if your child has avoided other sweets all day.

_____ 5. Replace the kitchen cookie jar with a bowl of fresh fruit.

_____ 6. Put your child on the diet that lets him lose 10 pounds.

_____ 7. Cook foods in non-stick fry pans.

_____ 8. Eliminate milk from your child's diet.

Preschool and Kindergarten Feeding Review

Here are some statements about feeding your preschool and kindergarten child. Circle *Yes* or *No* for each one.

1. Most preschool and kindergarten kids like bright-colored foods.　　　　　　　　　　　　Yes　　No

2. Your young child can learn simple table manners.　　　　　　　　　　　　Yes　　No

3. You should never allow your young child to have any sweets.　　　　　　　　　　　　Yes　　No

4. Your preschooler is too young to understand how different foods help different parts of her body.　　Yes　　No

5. An overweight kindergarten child is likely to grow up into an overweight adult.　　　　　　Yes　　No

6. Your preschool child will eat the same amount of food that your toddler ate.　　　　　　Yes　　No

7. Your young child should eat a little bit of every food that's served at family mealtime.　　　　Yes　　No

8. Don't try to get your overweight child to lose weight. Instead, try to slow down the rate at which he gains weight.　　　　　　　　　　　　Yes　　No

9. If your young child doesn't get many sweets at home, she probably won't stuff herself with junk foods once she starts school.　　　　　　　　　Yes　　No

10. Young kids enjoy growing their own vegetables.　　Yes　　No

Extra: Tell what is incorrect about each of the statements you circled *No* for.

III

GUIDANCE

One of your most important roles as a parent is to help your child be able to direct his or her own behavior. You want to guide your child into behavior that lets him enjoy life, be responsible, and get along well with other people.

You will provide *all* the guidance for your baby.

Your toddler still needs a lot of your guidance—you have to keep him safe, secure, and socially acceptable. But your toddler is beginning to learn how to choose on his own how to behave.

Your preschool and kindergarten child is ready to learn *self-guidance*. He'll start to use what he's learned from you about behavior to influence and guide his own actions, on his own.

BASICS OF EFFECTIVE GUIDANCE

Here's a list of suggestions about ways to guide your child's behavior. You can use these tips to guide your child in a positive, cooperative way. You have to use the tips according to your child's age and level of development, of course.

■ Be positive.

Say what to *do*, rather than what *not* to do. Say, "Jump on the floor," instead of, "Don't jump on the couch."

■ Be clear and specific.

Tell your child exactly what you want her to do or stop doing. "Behave yourself" or "Act your age" doesn't mean anything. "Talk quietly" tells your child you want him to talk rather than scream.

■ Don't threaten or bribe.

Threats and bribes don't work well. Surprise rewards, though, encourage a child.

■ **Show your child how to change behavior.**

When he kicks his brother, have him kick a ball instead. When she's teasing the cat, remove the cat and give her a favorite plaything instead.

■ **Don't make a big deal about a little thing.**

Spilled milk can be mopped up. Your child *will* make mistakes.

■ **Offer choices—but only when you mean it.**

Draw up a list of household chores, and let your child decide which ones he'll do. But don't offer your child a choice where there is none. At naptime, for example, just say, "It's naptime now," not, "Are you ready for your nap?"

■ **Praise efforts, not just results.**

Admire your child's efforts. This encourages her to keep on trying.

■ **Use "I" messages instead of "you" messages.**

"You" messages blame your child for something: "Look at what you've done!" "I" messages tell your child how you feel about what he's done: "Oh, what a mess. I want it cleaned up now."

■ **When you're wrong, admit it.**

Parents make mistakes, too, and kids know that. Your child will respect you when you admit you are wrong.

■ **Avoid direct conflict.**

You can force your child to do as you say, but he'll resent you for it. Try a cooperative approach instead. Find a solution that works for both of you. He won't eat broccoli? Ask him to name a green vegetable he will eat.

■ **Stay calm and matter-of-fact.**

Even if you're angry, don't shout, be insulting, or use physical threats. Tell your child what specific actions of hers have gotten you mad, and why.

■ **Accept your child's fears and anxieties.**

They may seem silly to you, but they are very real to your child. Give him love, and reassure him. The more secure he feels, the sooner the fears will disappear.

■ Let your child solve her own problems when possible.

You can offer help. But let your child find a solution to the problem whenever that's possible.

■ Set and enforce limits.

Your child feels secure when he knows you won't let him go too far. The limits must be clear and reasonable, though.

■ Have your child accept responsibility.

Actions have consequences. If she breaks her friend's toy airplane in a fit of rage, she'll have to give her friend one of her own toys in return.

To guide your child effectively, you have to know what kind of behavior to expect of the child at different ages and stages of the child's development. Some kind of behavior is just not possible for your child at certain stages. Effective guidance is different for babies, toddlers, and preschool/kindergarten children.

ACTIVITY

Using Effective Guidance

Here are some situations with parents and children. Which of the above-mentioned guidance suggestions is the parent using in each case? Write the suggestion(s) in the space after the situation.

1. Jamal is digging a hole in the lawn. His mother picks him up and places him in the sandbox. She says, "Dig a hole here, not on the lawn."

   _____

2. Anthony's daughter Gloria has thrown all of Anthony's shoes out of the closet and mixed them all up together in the middle of the bedroom floor. Anthony says, "Gloria, this gets me angry. I don't want all my shoes messed up. Put them back now."

   _____

3. Beatriz promised to rake all the leaves in the back yard. The job was much too big for her. Her father says, "Wow! Look at all the leaves you raked. You really worked hard."

   _____

(continued)

4. Brev cleaned his whole room without being told to do it. His mother is thrilled and says, "Let's goof off for the rest of the afternoon and go to the park."

_____

5. Emilio is splashing the water in the toilet bowl. His father stops him and says, "Emilio, you are not allowed to play with the toilet water. Would you like me to put water in the dishpan for you to play with instead?"

_____

GUIDANCE, DISCIPLINE, AND PUNISHMENT

What about *discipline*? Don't you have to discipline your child? Are discipline and guidance the same thing? That depends on how you define those words.

By guidance, we mean showing a child how to behave, influencing a child's behavior. You guide lovingly, and firmly when necessary. This is also one meaning of discipline.

But discipline can also mean punishing, and gaining control by making a person obey orders. Teaching by punishment doesn't work well.

In this section, we'll show you how to use guidance instead of punishment to teach your child how to behave.

What's wrong with using punishment to teach your child how to behave? Your child may develop a lot of anger and approach the world with a chip on his shoulder. He may become aggressive and try to force his wishes on other people, as you do with him. He may become fearful and passive, afraid to stand up for his rights in any situation. He may become sneaky and dishonest—he'll obey you when you're right there using your power over him, but he'll behave very differently when you're gone.

With guidance from you, your child becomes able to guide his own behavior. (Of course, he'll make a lot of mistakes along the way!) He feels good about doing what's right (most of the time).

With punishment, your child learns to obey only because and when she must. The older the child gets, the less she obeys. She hasn't learned self-discipline. She hasn't learned to be proud of acting responsibly, on her own.

ACTIVITY

Which Is It?

In each of these situations, decide whether the adult is using guidance or punishment.

1. Tanya, age 2, has been told over and over again not to play with the controls on the TV set. When Tanya fiddles with the TV anyway, she is scolded and spanked. Is this:

   Guidance _____   Punishment _____

2. Jaime, age 4, screams and refuses to get off Sasha's tricycle when Sasha wants a turn. Jaime's father picks Jaime up off the tricycle. He holds Jaime while Sasha takes her turn riding the tricycle. Is this:

   Guidance _____   Punishment _____

3. Akeem scribbles on the kitchen table. Akeem's mother gives Akeem some paper and tells him, "Draw on the paper, not on the table." Is this:

   Guidance _____   Punishment _____

4. Samantha, age 4½, was so excited about going to the circus that she wet her pants. Sam's parents are making her wear diapers for two days to be sure Sam feels ashamed of what she did and won't do it again. Is this:

   Guidance _____   Punishment _____

5. For each punishment situation above, suggest positive guidance approaches instead. Write your suggestions here:

   _____

   _____

   _____

   _____

   _____

   _____

Now role-play each situation in class. First use the punishment approach to the problem. Then use the guidance approach. Which seems to work best?

WHEN YOU'RE AT YOUR WITS' END

It's not easy being a parent! Sometimes you'll feel so stressed out, you'll feel like screaming at or even hitting your kids. Don't do it! Instead, try these ideas to relieve your stress.

- Take time out.
    Count to 10. Take 5 long, slow breaths. Recite the alphabet. Leave the room. Do some exercises.

Then:

- Spend some time apart from your kids.
    —Swap child-care time with other parents.
    —Find a local co-op or free child care.
    —Hire a babysitter for an hour or two.
    —Get a friend or relative to look after the kids once in a while.
    —Have the kids' other parent take care of them while you go out.

- Do things *for yourself* in your child-free time. (Don't do household chores or other work.)
    —Take a long, hot bath.
    —Take a long, quiet walk.
    —Exercise—dance around the room to fast music, do some jumping jacks, go out for a run or a bike ride.
    —Visit friends, or talk to them on the phone.
    —Go to a movie, or watch a video.
    —Eat at a restaurant.
    —Listen to your favorite music.
    —Read a book or magazine.
    —RELAX!

Guiding Your Baby
(Age: Birth to 1 Year)

Guiding a young baby is simple: You meet your baby's needs. From this, your baby learns to trust adults and feel secure. Your young baby's needs are very simple: She needs food, warmth and comfort, diaper changes, and affection.

As your baby gets older, she begins to use her body and her senses. You can help her do this by following the suggestions in the "Teaching Your Baby" section of this book.

The most important thing you need to know about guiding your baby's behavior is this: **A baby cannot learn to control his or her behavior**. You must not try to punish a baby. **Do not hit, slap, or shake your baby**. She will have no idea why you did that. She is simply too young to understand what you want. She can't deliberately choose to behave the way you want her to. Moreover, hitting, slapping, or shaking can seriously injure—or even kill—a baby.

Baby Guidance Tips

If your baby can't choose how to behave, how *do* you affect your baby's behavior?

- Find out what your baby needs, and fill that need. This makes your baby feel secure and willing to trust adults.
- Show your baby how pleased you are at something he's done. Smile, hug, talk happily. He'll feel good, and he'll want to please you more.
- Give your baby lots of attention. You make your baby feel good about herself. You meet her strong need for attention and affection. You help her learn how to communicate with other people, and give affection back.
- Show or tell your baby what you want her to do. Hold a plaything in front of her. Say, "Reach for the ball." As she reaches, say, "Yes! That's right! Get the ball."
- Arrange your baby's environment. Set things up so your baby will naturally do what you want. Take your baby out of the bathroom and put him in the playroom. Put unsafe items out of reach and surround your baby with things he can play with.

You can use these tips to deal with common baby behavior, like the following.

CRYING

Your baby has to cry. It's his only way of telling you that he needs something. He cries to let you know that he's hungry, wet, cold, uncomfortable, or tired. To stop the crying, you try to figure out what your baby needs and give it to him.

When you respond promptly to your baby's cries, he learns to trust you. He feels secure—he knows you'll take care of him. Later, when he's older, he'll be more willing to accept your guidance because he trusts you.

Spoiling

Can you spoil your young baby by answering his cries quickly? No. Babies thrive on love and affection. The more they get, the more they give. Your baby needs physical and social attention just as much as he needs food.

Fussy Babies

Unfortunately, almost every baby has a period of fussy crying every day. Also unfortunately, this fussy-crying period usually happens in the evening, when the baby's parents are tired and least able to cope with this crying. Follow the guidelines about what to do when your baby cries. If nothing works, then accept that you can't stop the crying.

Colic

About 10 or 15 babies out of every 100 develop colic. Babies with colic scream and double up with pain. They can't be comforted. They cry frantically for three to six hours, usually in the evening, *every* evening.

No one knows what causes colic. It goes away, on its own, by the time the baby is 3 months old.

You can't do much about colic. Follow the guidelines for soothing a fussy baby, get some relief from the crying, and tell yourself this won't last forever.

What to Do When Your Baby Cries

Your baby always cries for a reason. He can't tell you what he needs, of course. So you have to guess. Here's what to check for:

- Hunger. If he's hungry, feed him.
- Pain. Does he have gas? Or an air bubble in his stomach? Is a diaper pin sticking him? Pick him up and check him out.
- Cold. Babies don't like to be cold.
- Wet. A wet or soiled diaper may distress your baby.
- Need for physical contact or attention. Pick her up and cuddle her.
- Discomfort. Change her position.
- Boredom. Change the scenery. Give him interesting things to look at, grab for. Keep him near you so he can watch what you're doing.

How to Comfort a Very Fussy Baby

Try these ideas when your baby is very fussy.

- Wrap the baby snugly (not tightly) in a soft, light blanket.
- Walk around with your baby held snugly in your arms.
- Rock the baby.
- Carry the baby in a front carrier while you do things around the home.
- Use a windup swing. Be sure the baby's back and head are supported.
- Take the baby for a ride in a car or a baby carriage.
- Allow the baby to suck if she wants to. Help her find her hands, or offer her a pacifier.

ACTIVITY

Comforting Practice

Volunteer to help at a baby-care center. Or baby-sit for a baby. Or use your own baby for this exercise. Practice the different ways to soothe a crying baby. Record what happens here.

Number of Hours You Cared for Baby _____

Number of Crying Episodes (Times Baby Cried) _____

Cause of Each Crying Episode _____

_____

_____

Method You Used to Comfort Baby _____

_____

_____

SEPARATION ANXIETY

You are the most important person in the world to your baby. Her universe centers on you. Because you are all-important to her, she starts to want to keep you in her sight at every moment by the time she's around 8 months old. If you walk away from her, she'll crawl after you if she can. If she can't crawl, she'll fuss. If you leave the room and disappear from her sight, she'll howl.

It's called "separation anxiety" when your baby gets uneasy, sad, or even panicky when she's separated from you. This may seem ridiculous to you. But once you're out of sight, your baby doesn't know *if* you're coming back or *when* you're coming back.

Here's what to do about separation anxiety:

- Accept it as real. Try to stay within sight of your baby. Bring her from room to room with you, or let her crawl around after you.
- Don't avoid your baby or try to sneak away. He'll get even more anxious and watch you even more continually.
- Let your baby have a comforter, like a cuddly toy animal or much-loved blanket. Her comforter can make her feel secure when you're out of sight.
- Be sure your baby is used to someone else taking care of him. At least he will be less anxious if you have to leave him.
- Expect your baby to be fearful of strangers now, too. Don't hand her over to a stranger if she doesn't want to go.
- Play peek-a-boo with your baby.

ACTIVITY

Question

Why do you think playing peek-a-boo will help ease your baby's separation anxiety?

What to Do?

You're going out for the evening. A baby-sitter is staying with your 9-month-old baby. As you start to go out the door, your baby starts to sob and cry frantically. What do you do?

DIFFERENT BABIES, DIFFERENT NEEDS

Children, teenagers, adults—no two are alike. No two babies are exactly alike, either. Some babies are very fussy. Some babies sleep peacefully between feedings. Some babies are wakeful, alert, and very active. Others are quiet.

You need to keep these differences in mind when you're handling your baby. One baby may jump, become startled, and cry at the least disturbance. You have to handle this baby very gently and quietly. Another baby kicks, squirms, and seems to be in motion all the time. You'll want to handle this baby more actively—bounce him on your knees, do arm and leg "exercises" with him (see page 104, under "Body Moves"), carry him around with you.

Take care of your baby in whatever way seems best for *her*. If it makes her happy and contented, do it. You're building the basis of trust and love that you'll need for the next, very demanding stage of child development: the toddler years.

Baby Guidance Review

Here are some statements about babies. Circle *Yes* or *No* for each one.

1. If you pick up your baby every time she cries, you'll spoil her. — Yes   No
2. A wet diaper may cause a baby to become uncomfortable and start crying. — Yes   No
3. Babies don't get bored. — Yes   No
4. Teach your baby not to cry so much by scolding him when he cries between meals. — Yes   No
5. Bouncing and other active play will make a baby cry. — Yes   No
6. Giving your baby lots of attention helps your baby feel good about herself. — Yes   No
7. Sometimes there's nothing you can do that will stop your baby's crying. — Yes   No
8. A baby with colic cries every evening for about half an hour. — Yes   No
9. When you respond to your baby's cries, you teach him to trust adults. — Yes   No
10. You can teach your baby how to behave if you know the right things to do. — Yes   No

Extra: Tell what is incorrect about each of the statements you circled *No* for.

Guiding Your Toddler
(Age: 1 year to 3 years)

Your toddler is a very contradictory person. He's learning to be independent, but he depends on you for security. He's a bold and tireless explorer, and he's a fearful, clingy baby. He loves to help and please you, but he says "No!" when you ask him to do something.

Life with a toddler means accepting these ups and downs, these mood changes. You need to be flexible and understanding. Your toddler is trying to do things for herself. She's learning not to depend on you, her parents, for everything. But she's still a very young child. She makes mistakes, knocks things over, breaks things that are breakable. She gets frustrated about the things she can't do.

TODDLER GUIDANCE TIPS

How do you guide this little bundle of energy and contradictions? First, remember that your toddler is still very immature. He can't always remember the rules you set down. He can't always make himself follow the rules even when he does remember them. So follow these guidelines for guiding your toddler:

- Praise your toddler when he does something you like, something that pleases you, something that practices a skill he's learning.

- Create safe surroundings for your toddler to explore freely so you don't punish her for normal toddler behavior. (If you leave the sugar bowl out on the table, your toddler *will* play with it, no matter what you tell her.)

- Set reasonable and consistent limits, and stick to them. Your toddler can't remember and follow a lot of rules. But when your toddler does something unacceptable—like biting the baby—stop that behavior right away, and tell why you don't like what he's doing.

- Be ready to demonstrate over and over again what is acceptable and what is unacceptable behavior. You can stick to the limits, but your toddler can't. Stay calm and loving. A sense of humor helps!

- Continue to offer love, security, and affection. When your toddler is acting most unlovable may be the moment when she needs your loving the most. But let your toddler choose when she wants to be cuddled and babied.

Your toddler *must* separate from you and learn to cope with the world on his own. But this is scary for him.

Your toddler's drive for independence fuels most of the guidance problems you'll face at this stage: negativism, temper tantrums, fears, and emotional outbursts. Welcome to the "terrible twos"!

NEGATIVISM—OR, JUST SAYING "NO!" (NO, NO, NO . . .)

Your toddler is learning to be independent, to be separate from you. He's deciding *what* to do, *when* to do it, and *how* to do it. He wants to do things his way, not your way. Try to tell him, or even suggest to him, what to do. You'll get a very positive "No!"

Also, your toddler is programmed to be curious, to get into everything, to *explore*. She'll be noisy, she'll get dirty, she'll knock things over and break things. She'll push past all your limits.

What to Do

Don't take it personally. Remember that a toddler *has* to act independently yet also needs you to keep him safe and within some limits. Try these ideas:

- Don't offer choices when you don't mean it. If you ask, "Do you want to eat supper now?" your toddler will say "No!" Instead, say, "It's time for supper now."

- Do offer small choices when you can. "Do you want to wear your yellow pajamas or your green pajamas tonight?" No chance for a "No!" answer.

- Make your toddler want to do what you want him to do. If you say, "Put your cars away now," he'll say, "No!" Instead, say, "I'll bet you can't put your cars into their garage before I change the sheets on your bed!" Now it's a game.

- Distract your toddler. If she keeps going back to that electric outlet, remove her from the room. Take Aunt Wilma's glass vase away and give him a plastic pitcher instead.

What Works Best?

Here are some situations with toddlers. For each one, which parent statement do you think would get the best behavior result from the toddler? Check your choice.

1. It's cold outside. Your toddler needs to wear something warm. What do you say?

 ___ "You have to wear your coat if you go outside."

 ___ "Do you want to wear your sweater or your coat?"

2. Your toddler's room is a mess, and you want it cleaned up. What do you say?

 ___ "I'll pick up the dolls. You pick up the blocks."

 ___ "You have to clean your room before you can watch TV."

3. It's bedtime. What do you say?

 ___ "It's time for bed now."

 ___ "Are you ready to go to bed now?"

 ___ "You must be sleepy. I'll bet you want to go to bed."

4. Your toddler sees a glass pitcher of lemonade on the table. She starts toward it. You're on the other side of the room. What do you say?

 ___ "No, no! Don't touch the lemonade."

 ___ "Nathan! Look at what I have for you over here."

Real-Life Practice

Now practice these techniques with a real toddler. What does seem to work best?

EMOTIONAL OUTBURSTS

Your toddler gets frustrated a lot as he tries to do things for himself. He isn't physically able to do what he wants. Or you won't let him do what he wants. He tries to tell you something, but you can't understand what he's saying.

Frustrated, he bursts into tears. It's a natural way to relieve his tension. Just be sure there are lots of things he *can* do.

You can also expect your toddler to cry and get emotionally upset when she's tired or hungry. Keep her on an even keel with regular mealtimes and early bedtimes. Don't expect her to behave well on long shopping trips or lengthy restaurant meals. She can't!

TEMPER TANTRUMS

As we just said, life is frustrating for your toddler. When too much frustration builds up inside him, it explodes in a temper tantrum. Your toddler screams, yells, thrashes around, and pounds the floor.

Temper tantrums are scary for you *and* for your toddler. He's scared because he's out of control with violent feelings. You're scared he might hurt himself, and he may be turning blue from holding his breath. You're probably angry, too, that he's behaving so outrageously. Here are some things you can do:

- Ignore the tantrum. Keep your distance. Go on with what you're doing.
- Stay calm. Don't get into a shouting match—you'll just keep the tantrum going.
- Keep your toddler from hurting herself or hurting anyone or anything else.
- Gently hold and comfort your toddler during the tantrum if she'll let you.
- Go back to normal activities with your toddler once the tantrum is over.
- Ignore the tantrum even if your toddler's face turns blue from breath holding. (His body will force him to start breathing again before any damage is done.)

ACTIVITY

Handling Outbursts and Tantrums

How would you handle these situations? Check each action you think would work well. (More than one action might work.)

1. Angela throws a temper tantrum in the supermarket when her mother refuses to buy the cereal Angela wants. Angela's mother:
   ___ a. Picks up the screaming child and carries her out of the store.
   ___ b. Tells Angela to stop crying or she will be punished when she gets home.
   ___ c. Spanks Angela to stop the tantrum.

(continued)

2. Matt bursts into tears when he can't fit the last piece into his jigsaw puzzle. Matt's caregiver:

   ___ a. Helps Matt guide the piece into place.

   ___ b. Scolds Matt for getting upset about nothing.

   ___ c. Gives Matt a puzzle he can do.

3. Roberto bursts into a temper tantrum when his father says Roberto can't go to the park today. Roberto's father:

   ___ a. Shouts louder so Roberto can hear him.

   ___ b. Goes into another room, ignoring Roberto.

   ___ c. Stops Roberto from banging his head on the floor.

   ___ d. Decides to go to the park after all, since Roberto wants so much to do that.

Real-Life Observation

Watch a toddler who is throwing a temper tantrum in public. Observe how the toddler's parent or caregiver handles the situation. Does the parent follow our guidelines? If not, what does the parent do? What effect does the parent's action have on the toddler, if any?

FEARS

As your toddler becomes more independent and explores the world around her, she meets many things that frighten her. This is natural. A young child can't protect herself from danger. She fears strange things because they may be harmful. The fear makes her turn to her parents or caregiver for protection. The fear is a built-in safety net.

When fear turns your toddler to you for comfort and protection, give it to her. Her fear may seem wildly unreasonable, even silly, to you. She may be afraid of clocks, or shower curtains. But the fear is real and very scary for her. Handle it carefully and kindly.

If you call your toddler's fears "silly," he won't believe you. He'll feel even more scared because he doesn't have your support and comfort.

- Accept the fear, whether it's reasonable to you or not.

- Comfort your fearful toddler.

- Tell your child there is nothing to fear if the thing will not hurt him. But don't make him go near or touch the thing he's afraid of.

Once your toddler learns from his own willing experience that a thing won't hurt him, his fear will go away.

ACTIVITY

Common Toddler Fears

Separate with your classmates into groups of three or four. Make a list of what you think are the four or five most common fears of toddlers. Compare your group's list with other groups' lists. What does the class as a whole think toddlers are most likely to be afraid of? Write them here:

1. _____
2. _____
3. _____
4. _____
5. _____

WHEN THERE'S A NEW BABY

When a new baby joins the family, your toddler, preschooler, or kindergartner will be jealous. He'll be curious, too. He'll probably also show some affection. But he's sure to worry about sharing—or losing—your love and affection. To get your young child off to a good start with his new baby brother or sister, try these ideas:

- Tell your young child *ahead of time* about the baby.

- Let your young child know who will take care of him while Mommy is in the hospital. Let him visit Mommy in the hospital if possible.

- Let your young child help with the baby *if he wants to*. Even a 3-year-old can do useful things, like bring you a fresh diaper.

- Spend time alone with your young child, when you can give him all your attention.

- Let your young child act babyish once in a while. Let him try a bottle if he wants. He'll decide pretty quickly that he prefers drinking from a cup instead, like grownups.

- Let your young child express his jealous feelings. Let him know you understand. But:

- Do not let your young child hurt the baby.

PLAYING WITH OTHER TODDLERS

Your toddler is expanding her world. She's ready to get used to other children her age (her peers). This doesn't mean she's ready to play *with* other children. She's only able to play *alongside* them. She'll play her own games while also watching what the other child is doing, getting new ideas for her own play.

Grabbing

You'll have to wait for your child to be 3 or 4 before he can learn to share and take turns. A toddler can't do this. He'll hang on to the toy he's playing with. He'll grab the toy he wants away from another child.

What You Can Do. Expect this. Run interference: Let the children play next to each other and keep them from taking each other's toys or destroying each other's creations. Bit by bit, as they get older, they'll learn to share.

Biting, Hitting, Pushing

Toddlers aren't mature enough to play together very well. They can't share or take turns. They can't even talk well enough to tell each other what they want or don't like. So when they want their playmate to do something, or stop doing something, they may use "body language." They push or hit or even bite their playmate.

This may look like naked aggression to you. But the toddler doesn't know he's hurting his playmate. He's just showing how he feels.

What You Can Do. Be alert when toddlers play together. Separate them when they quarrel. Explain that a playmate hurts when she's pushed or hit. (If your toddler almost always bites or hits other children she's with, think about what may be wrong. She's not used to other children? Her life at home is full of "no's" so she's terribly tense and frustrated? She's jealous of the new baby? What can you do to ease these problems?)

ACTIVITY

Question

Parents often wonder, "When my child bites, should I bite back to show my child that biting hurts?" What do you think? What positive effect could biting back have? What negative effects? Write your ideas here:

Positive Effects   *Negative Effects*

_____   _____

_____   _____

_____   _____

_____   _____

_____   _____

_____   _____

_____   _____

Share your ideas with classmates in a class discussion.

Real-Life Observation

Volunteer at a day-care center, or observe toddlers at play in a public park. Do you notice the characteristics of toddler play—playing alongside, grabbing, pushing? Record what you notice. Compare your observations with what your classmates saw.

Toddler Guidance Review

Here are some situations involving toddler guidance. Circle *Yes* or *No* for each one.

1. You give your toddler and her little cousin a dump truck to play with and tell them to take turns. Yes   No

2. Your toddler is afraid of being in the bathtub. You decide to give her sponge baths in the sink for a while instead. Yes   No

3. You happen to notice your toddler putting his books on the shelf. You say, "Oh, good! It's so nice to see all the books on the shelf." Yes   No

4. Your toddler knows she is not allowed to dump her toys into the baby's playpen. You can count on her to remember and follow this rule. Yes   No

5. Your toddler says she doesn't like the new baby and wants to get rid of it. You're shocked and tell her that of course she loves the new baby and doesn't mean what she's saying. Yes   No

6. You have a pretty display of blue glass vases in the picture window. You are very angry that your toddler keeps touching the vases. You punish her each time she does it. Yes   No

7. You have to leave for the hospital at 2 a.m. to have your new baby. You wake up your toddler to tell him you're going and that Aunt Sue is here to stay with him. Yes   No

8. You pick up your toddler at the day-care center. You want her to know you've missed her all day. So you cuddle her all the way home even though she keeps squirming away. Yes   No

Extra: Tell what is incorrect about each of the statements you circled *No* for.

Guiding Your Preschool and Kindergarten Child (Age: 3 years to 5 years)

By age 3 or so, your child has passed through the troubled waters of toddlerhood. She's ready to control her own behavior (most of the time). She can play cooperatively with other children her age (without too many quarrels). She's confident about feeling independent, and doesn't worry about daily separations from her parents.

Perhaps the most delightful change you'll notice in your young child is this: He wants to please you, and he wants to be like you. Your toddler seemed determined to do whatever you *didn't* want him to do. He certainly didn't choose his actions to get praise from you. But your preschool and kindergarten child does—most of the time, anyway. He wants your approval. He wants you to be pleased with him. So take this opportunity to help your child learn to help around the house, put toys away, use good table manners.

INDEPENDENCE AND LIMITS

Your toddler struggled to learn how to be independent. Your preschool and kindergarten child has learned independence. He knows he can do a lot of things for himself. He's interested in playing with other children his own age, not being with you all the time. He's gotten control of his body. Now he wants to test his body in all sorts of physical activities.

Your main challenge in guiding your preschool and kindergarten child is dealing with her growing independence. You need to allow her as much independence as she can handle. But at the same time you must set and stick to definite limits.

By the age of 3 or so, your child can understand limits. He knows even more about limits by the time he's 4 or 5. He can learn to keep his behavior within these limits (most of the time). What kind of limits?

- Safety limits. You still need to help your child keep himself safe. Let him climb the jungle gym—he needs to discover his physical abilities. But keep him from playing in the street.

- Protection-of-other-people limits. You have to help your child learn how to play cooperatively without hurting other people, or other people's things.

- Social rules limits. You have to teach your child how to behave acceptably around other people.

ACTIVITY

Social Rules

With classmates, brainstorm a list of types of social behavior you think preschool and kindergarten children should be taught. Write your list here:

_____   _____

_____   _____

Follow-Through

Once you've set the limits for your young child's behavior, you must stick to these limits. You must be consistent. *Each time* your child goes beyond a limit, you must step in and stop the unacceptable behavior. Be firm, not angry.

Tell your child what you want him to stop doing, and what you want him to do instead. Then make sure he does what you said. You may need to guide him physically away from the unacceptable behavior: "Billy, stop throwing pebbles at Sam. Put the pebbles in your pail instead." If Billy keeps throwing pebbles, go over to him and lead him away from the pebbles. Get him started on another activity. When you see him doing something you like, praise him: "What a nifty castle you and Sam made with those pebbles!"

ACTIVITY

Real-Life Observation

Go to a public park or playground. Watch and listen to young children and their parents/caregivers. Look for cases of follow-through and no follow-through. What happens when the parent/caregiver says, "Johnny, stop that," over and over again, but doesn't actually do anything to stop Johnny? Collect four or five of these little dramas. Then share what you've observed with your classmates. Use this space to make notes on what you observe.

_____

_____

FEARS

Your toddler feared a lot of real things—dogs, snakes, loud noises. Your preschool and kindergarten child is a bundle of imagination. He's likely to worry about all kinds of things that *might* happen. He sees a burning house on the TV news. What if his house burns down? He hears a story about a car crash. What if Mommy crashes her car? He hears someone mention death. Will he die too?

In particular, your young child is likely to worry about getting hurt. She's become very aware of her body—she *is* her body. So she's fearful of injuring that body. (She'll still play boisterously, though.) She'll clamor for bandages for even the tiniest cut.

These fears about wholeness and injury can make your preschooler fear any kind of breaking. She won't accept a broken cookie. She'll refuse to play with an armless doll.

How do you and your young child live with these fears?

- Let your child talk about her fears. Don't make fun of her. If you talk to your child a lot, she'll find it easy to talk to you—even about things she's afraid of.

- Reassure your child. Be understanding, and let her know you will protect her from danger.

- Let him act out the fears if that seems to help. If he's worried about robbers, let him play-act chasing robbers out of your home.

- Figure out what may be causing stress in your child's life. Does she have enough active, vigorous play to blow off tensions? (Make sure she does.) Are you battling with him over eating or toilet training? (Ease off.) Is he upset by family problems or illness? (Talk about it.)

PLAYING WITH OTHER CHILDREN

Your toddler played alongside other children. Your preschooler is ready to play *with* other children. They'll build block houses together. They'll be fire fighters racing to put out a blaze.

Playing with other children teaches your young child the important skills of sharing and taking turns. It's not easy for a young child to learn to share a favorite toy with someone else. It's not easy to wait while someone gets to use the swing.

- If your child isn't used to group play, start slowly. Have just a few—2 or 3—children play together at first.
- Help your child see what he does or doesn't do that causes group-play problems. Suggest other ways to act.
- If your child is going to play with a friend at home, let her put away some toys she won't want to share.
- Praise your child when you see her sharing or taking turns: "Luisa, I liked the way you let Bobby go down the slide first."
- If your child is very aggressive—hitting, kicking, biting—ask yourself why. Is he bossed around and ruled by an older sibling? Is he jealous of a new baby? Do you use physical punishments to keep him in line? Reduce these stresses in his life.
- Help your child understand that other people's feelings are like his. How does he feel when the other children won't let him join them in the sandbox? That's exactly how Sondra feels when he keeps her out. This is not obvious to your child at first.

ACTIVITY

Guiding Group Play

What would you do in each of these situations to help the young child play more easily with other children?

1. Heather always insists on being in charge of games. The other children avoid playing with Heather.
2. Whenever he's with a group of other children, Juan suddenly bites one of his playmates.
3. Nicky loves his toy fire engine. He screams and cries when his friend Kate tries to play with it.
4. Teresa hasn't played much with other children. Now she's at day care with 12 other kids.

Real-Life Guidance

Volunteer to help out at a preschool or kindergarten. Use the guidelines to help the children in their cooperative play.

SIBLING RIVALRY

A sibling is a brother or sister. The term "sibling rivalry" refers to the jealous feelings brothers and sisters have about each other. They see each other as rivals for their parents' attention and affection.

Once the baby grows into a young child herself, you can expect plenty of squabbles and fights between your children. As they learn to get along with each other, they learn to get along with the rest of the world. But sibling squabbles can drive a parent crazy! Try these ideas to help your children get along with each other:

- *Never* compare one child with another. That just makes the child more jealous.

- Don't encourage competition between siblings. You want your kids to be friends, not rivals. You want them to play together and learn to support each other, not try to best each other.

- Let each child know you value and accept him for who he is.

- Don't take sides in sibling fights. Keep them from hurting each other, but make them work out the argument themselves. If you take sides, they've got a good reason to keep on quarreling, hoping to see the rival sibling get a scolding.

TV VIEWING

It's important to limit the amount of TV watching your young child does.

First, watching TV is a *passive* activity. Your child isn't doing anything; she's just sitting there. Kids need to be active with people and things in order to learn. They need lots of physical activity to develop their bodies. And they need to exercise their brains and imaginations. TV viewing stops all this.

Second, TV shows a lot of violence, and other scenes that can frighten and worry young children. A 4- or 5-year-old child can't tell for sure what's real and what's make-believe on TV. So you need to choose shows carefully. It's best to watch TV with your young child so you can explain and reassure when she sees something that troubles or confuses her.

Follow these tips to guide your young child's TV viewing:

- You decide which shows your young child may watch.
- Turn the TV on for your child to watch only when a show you've chosen is on.
- Turn the TV off when the show is over.
- If older people in the family are watching other shows, try to keep your child entertained in another room.
- Don't use the TV as an "electronic babysitter"—something mindless to keep your child quiet.

ACTIVITY

TV for Young Children

In class, make a list of TV shows your children might watch. Watch those shows at home for several weeks. Back in class, decide which TV shows you think are good or okay for young children to watch, and which are not. Write here the names of those shows.

TV Shows—Acceptable	Okay to Watch?	Good to Watch?
_____	☐	☐
_____	☐	☐
_____	☐	☐
_____	☐	☐
_____	☐	☐

TV Shows—Not Acceptable	Why It's Not Acceptable
_____	_____
_____	_____
_____	_____
_____	_____
_____	_____

Now discuss how much TV you think a young child should watch.

Hours per day: _____

Hours per week: _____

Preschool and Kindergarten Guidance Review

Here are some statements about guiding the behavior of a preschool or kindergarten child. Circle *Yes* or *No* for each one.

1. Stop your young child from trying to climb that tree. She could get hurt, and you need to protect her.   Yes   No

2. Your young child is old enough to learn how to take care of his own things.   Yes   No

3. When your young child worries about your house burning down, assure her that this won't happen.   Yes   No

4. It's silly for your young child to get very upset about a cut finger.   Yes   No

5. Keep out of your children's arguments with each other.   Yes   No

6. A young child can learn some valuable things from TV. Even so, he shouldn't watch very much TV.   Yes   No

7. You should teach your young child not to knock down his playmate's tower of blocks or sand castle.   Yes   No

8. Your preschool or kindergarten child is too young to learn how to behave properly in public places.   Yes   No

9. When your young child is doing something you don't like, keep telling her, "Stop that!" over and over until she does stop.   Yes   No

10. When your young child misbehaves, point out his older sister's good behavior as a model.   Yes   No

Extra: Tell what is incorrect about each of the statements you circled *No* for.

IV

TEACHING YOUR CHILD

PLAY AND LEARNING

"Play is a child's work."

What does that mean?

A child's "job" is to learn. Think of all the things a child needs to learn!

- A baby has to learn to use his hands and understand messages from his eyes, ears, and skin.
- A toddler has to learn how to walk, run, and talk and understand how the things in her world work.
- A preschool and kindergarten child has to master complicated physical tasks like tying shoelaces. He has to learn perplexing social tasks like sharing time and space with other people.

How does a child work at this job of learning? By playing. Your child's play teaches her all these many, many things she needs to learn. The skills your child learns as a baby, toddler and young child prepare her for later childhood and, eventually, adult life. Through play, your child develops mentally and physically, emotionally and socially.

You can help as your child learns. This is one of a parent's or caregiver's most important functions!

In the previous section, we discussed ways to guide your baby and young child in how to behave and get along with other people. In this section of the book, we talk about ways to help your child—as a baby, toddler, and young child—develop her body and mind.

When you teach your child, or guide his learning, you must always keep in mind your child's age, or level of development. Your child can only learn what he's physically or mentally able to learn at any particular stage. You can't get a 6-month-old baby to learn his ABC's! But you *can* help him learn to sit up.

Helping Your Baby Learn
(Age: Birth to 1 year)

YOUR BABY DEVELOPS

(These are the *average* ages at which babies develop certain abilities.
Individual babies will do things at different ages.)

AGE	SKILLS	
Birth/ 1 month	Looks at faces. Hands are in fists. Can see, but vision is blurry. Cries to express discomfort. Responds to sudden loud noises.	
3 months	Holds up head when lying on stomach. Swipes at toys. Plays with hands. Looks at faces. Recognizes primary caregiver. Makes sounds of pleasure.	Smiles. May roll over.
6 months	Sits with support. Reaches for and grasps objects. Puts everything into mouth. Laughs and babbles. Rolls over.	Uses thumbs.
9 months	Sits without help. Pulls to standing. Feeds self finger foods. Understands simple words. Grips small objects with thumb and finger. Knows difference between strangers and familiar people.	Crawls.
12 months (1 Year)	Stands alone. Climbs up and down stairs. Says some simple words. Walks while holding onto furniture. Drops and places one object into another.	Crawls rapidly.

EARLY LEARNING THROUGH SIGHT AND SOUND

Your baby's first learning experiences come through his senses—especially seeing, hearing, and touching. Your baby learns about people and

things—the world around him—through his senses. First your baby hears and sees things. Then he reaches for and touches them.

Since your baby learns through his senses, you need to fill his world with things his senses can react to. Give your baby brightly colored objects with interesting shapes to *look at*. Give him interesting sounds to *listen to*. When he's a few months old, put different things nearby that he can *reach for* and *touch*. (We'll talk about touch later in this section, in "Finding and Using the Hands.")

Things to Look at

ACTIVITY

Question

Can you guess what single thing a young baby most likes to look at? Write your guess here:

_____

Then find the answer in the list of guidelines below. Were you right?

Since your new baby can't do much more than lie in her crib and look around, it's important to give her interesting things to look at. Follow these guidelines:

- Keep objects about 10" from baby's eyes. (Young babies can't see very far.)

- Put objects off to baby's side, not right above her. (Young babies mostly look to the side, especially the right side.)

- Hang mobiles with interesting shapes and colors— especially shapes with features that look like human faces.

- Keep light dim until your baby is about 8 weeks old.

- Give baby some slowly moving objects to look at. (For example: balloons, strips of crepe paper, foil pie plates.)

- Add a mirror (7" from eyes) when your baby is around 8 or 9 weeks old.

- Move baby around—change the scenery! Move her from crib to chest carrier to baby seat, from room to room, indoors and out.

- Change the objects for your baby to look at often.

ACTIVITY

Make a Mobile

Make a mobile for a young baby, following the guidelines you just read. Bring your mobile to school for a class display.

Evaluate Mobiles

Look at some mobiles that are for sale in baby or toy stores. Do they fit our guidelines? Which guidelines don't they fit?

Things to Listen to

ACTIVITY

Question

What natural sound seems to soothe newborn babies most? Write your answer here:

_____

Your new baby can hear quite well. Rhythmic sounds and music will soothe and relax him. Try these ideas to stimulate your baby's sense of hearing:

- Play recorded songs with simple, repeated rhythms—like lullabies or folk songs.
- Sing songs to your baby, or play a guitar, or harmonica, or other musical instrument for him.
- Avoid sudden loud sounds—your baby will jump, or "startle," and then probably start crying.
- *Talk* to your baby, a lot. He loves the sound of your pleasant and friendly voice. (Read more about this in "Learning About Language" later in this section.)

ACTIVITY

Sound in the Womb

Can unborn babies hear sound? Do some research on this. Ask mothers of babies what they think. Did they ever notice their unborn baby react to sound? Share the information you gather in a class discussion.

LEARNING TO USE THE BODY

It takes a while for your baby to discover the different parts of her body, and then to learn how to use them. Your baby can see and hear at birth, automatically. But she can't use her hands right away. At first, she doesn't even know she *has* hands!

Head Control

Your new baby is top-heavy! She can't hold her head up because her head is too heavy and her neck muscles are too weak. You have to hold her head steady for her. By the age of 3 months, your baby will have better control of her head.

How You Can Help. Put baby on her stomach often. Lying on her stomach, she'll practice lifting up her head. As she practices lifting, she'll strengthen her neck and shoulder muscles.

Body Moves

As soon as he's born, your baby can move his arms, legs, and body. But he can't control these moves. As his muscles develop, he gradually learns to control his body movements.

How You Can Help. Do arm and leg "exercises" with your baby. Stretch his arms out and back in (gently!). Move his legs as though he's pedaling a bicycle. Let him lie on you and roll off (on a soft surface). Let him push his legs against your hands. Pull him up slowly to a sitting position, letting him do as much of the sitting-up work as possible.

Rolling Over

If your baby is very active, he'll probably roll over when he's 2 or 3 months old. If he's not quite so active, he'll probably roll over at 4 or 5 months. A baby usually rolls from tummy to back first. Rolling over can start at any time, with no warning. So don't leave your "nonrolling" baby on top of anything he can fall from, like a bed or changing table.

How You Can Help. Put an object your baby would like to get to off to her side. Give her room to roll by laying her down on a pad on the floor.

Finding and Using the Hands

In the first two months of life, your baby's hands stay curled up into fists most of the time. At around 8 weeks old, your baby's hands begin to open up and the baby discovers these fascinating new playthings. Soon you'll notice that your baby spends a lot of time playing with her hands, watching them as she does. She begins "swiping" at nearby objects. Next she reaches out for the objects. Once she can grasp things (this takes lots of practice), she immediately explores her "finds" with her mouth.

How You Can Help

■ **Rattles.**

Once your baby starts to open his hands, give him toys he can grasp that make a sound. The sound will make him notice what his hands are doing.

■ **Hanging objects.**

When she's ready, give your baby some hanging objects to swipe at—a foam rubber ball, say, or a rattle. She's developing "eye-hand coordination"—the ability to look at sommething and then reach it with her hand (or foot). She's learning about cause and effect too—when she touches something (the cause), the object moves (the effect).

■ **Cradle gym.**

Once your baby can grasp a hanging object (not just swipe at it), give him a "cradle gym": objects to grasp and pull that are attached to a wooden rod or heavy belting hung across the crib. Be sure the objects don't swing very much. To practice getting hold of things successfully, your baby needs nonmoving objects.

■ **Objects to handle.**

When your baby is sitting up (in your lap, in his infant seat, or on his own), be sure lots of safe objects are within his reach. This gives him lots of the practice he needs in reaching out and getting hold of things. Remember that whatever he does reach will go right to his mouth!

ACTIVITY

Make a Cradle Gym

Following our guidelines, make a cradle gym for a baby. Bring your cradle gym to class for a group display. Then try your cradle gym out on a real baby!

(continued)

Is It Safe?

You must be sure that any object your baby can reach is safe for the baby to handle and put in her mouth. What objects might be safe? What objects might not be safe? List four or five of each. Share your list with classmates.

Safe Objects for *Baby to Handle*	*Unsafe Objects for* *Baby to Handle*
_____	_____
_____	_____
_____	_____
_____	_____

Sitting Up

Sometime between around 6 and 9 months old, your baby will learn to sit up without help. In a sitting position, with her hands free, your baby can play and learn in many new and more interesting ways than she could while lying down.

How You Can Help. Your baby *wants* to sit; it's the next step in her built-in development schedule. But she can't practice sitting at first because she can't get up into the sitting position. She needs you to put her into position. Her balance won't work at first, so she'll fall over a lot. Cushion her falls by putting soft padding all around her (like pillows and quilts) until she gets the hang of this new skill.

Crawling

Around 9 months old (often earlier, often later), your baby will learn how to crawl. He can make his way across a room using his arms and legs. Babies use many different styles of crawling. You may be surprised at the one your baby develops!

How You Can Help. Give your baby a roomy, safe place to crawl in. (No splintery floors, dangerous objects, stairs to fall down.) Put interesting objects partway across the room that he'll want to get to. Expect him to get grubby while he crawls.

Crawling Styles

Observe a group of crawling babies. How many different crawling styles do the babies use? Describe them here:

_____

_____

_____

_____

_____

Now take turns with your classmates demonstrating the different baby-crawling styles you've found.

Standing

Around 11 or 12 months, your baby will discover the thrill of pulling herself up to a standing position. Then she'll start "cruising"—stepping sideways while holding onto something. Soon she'll be walking!

How You Can Help. At first, your baby may not be able to sit down once she's standing. Hold her hands and gently lower her to a sitting position. Soon she'll learn to do this on her own. Also: Be sure anything your baby will pull herself up on will not fall over on her. Keep her feet bare, or use slipper socks with nonslip soles.

Safe Standing

Suppose you had a pulling-up-to-stand baby in your home. Study your living room and kitchen and list here the dangerous things your baby could pull up on. How could you make them safe?

LEARNING ABOUT LANGUAGE

In the first year of her life, your baby learns a lot about language, even though she can't talk yet. She listens to what you're saying. Bit by bit, she begins to understand what your words mean. She starts making language-type sounds herself. So it's important to talk to your baby a lot.

You want your baby to understand real language. And you want her to learn to speak real language. So talk normally to your baby, most of the time, instead of using made-up "baby talk."

It's also important to read to your baby. Share simple picture books with him. He'll love the pictures. You can read the words, or just talk about what you both see on each page. Either way, your baby learns more about language—about what words describe which things. He also learns to enjoy books.

ACTIVITY

Baby Books

Go to your local library. Find some books to read or share with a baby. Try them out with a real baby. Bring the books to class. What does the class think makes a book good for a baby? Write what you decide here:

_____

_____

_____

_____

_____

THINGS TO PLAY WITH

Once your baby can sit up without help, she can play in much more interesting ways. She'll enjoy throwing and dropping things, over and over again. She'll like things that roll, both balls and wheeled toys. She'll happily spend time putting things into containers and then dumping them out.

Give your sitting baby a few toys at a time to play with. When he gets bored, put those toys away and give him some other ones. For your crawling baby, set up some drawers, shelves, and baskets filled with things he can pull out and play with.

Your baby plays with something to find out what it's all about. Can he squeeze it? Does it make a noise? Does it roll? Does it bounce?

Once he's satisfied his curiosity about the object, he loses interest in it, for now. So you always need new and different things for your baby to play with. This could get expensive! But it doesn't have to be. Simple household objects make delightful baby playthings.

ACTIVITY

Household Toys

What household items would make interesting and appropriate playthings for a baby? List 9 here. Share your list with classmates.

_____   _____   _____

_____   _____   _____

_____   _____   _____

GOING PLACES

Your baby needs lots of changes of scenery. She needs to see and be part of different surroundings. Changes of scenery stimulate your baby's senses and chase away her boredom. Just moving her from room to room gives her an ever-changing series of worlds.

You want to take your baby outside your home, too. She'll become aware of the outside world. She'll learn to be sociable with people other than her own family members. She'll see many new and exciting things.

How do you move your baby around and take him places without carrying him in your arms all the time? Our inventive world offers you many clever devices for moving and carrying your baby.

■ Chest carrier.

A soft fabric carrier with a stiff head support. You carry your baby snuggled up against your chest. (Age: Birth to 4 or 5 months.)

■ Backpack.

A fabric seat attached to a metal frame. Your child sits in the seat as you carry him on your back. (Age: 3 months to 2½–3 years.) Don't use a backpack until your baby can hold his head up without support.

■ Infant seat.

A molded plastic seat with a stand, safety strap, and padded liner. It holds your baby in a semi-upright position while she's too young to sit up by herself. (Age: Birth to about 6 months.)

■ Carriage.

A baby bed raised up on a frame with wheels, with a fold-down hood. You push your lying-down (perhaps sleeping) baby along in front of you as you walk. (Age: Birth to about 6 months.)

■ Stroller.

A baby seat on wheels, usually with an adjustable seat, a fold-back canopy, and a rack for packages. You push your seated baby/young child in front of you as you walk along. (Age: 3 months to 3–4 years.)

■ Car carriers and seats.

Always use one of these—see "Your Baby's Safety" in the first section of the book.

ACTIVITY

Safety First

Here are some safety checklists for baby-carrying gear. Write the name of each item in the blank below its safety checklist.

chest carrier	carriage
backpack	stroller
infant seat	car carrier/seat

1. Must be stable, not tippy; must have strap to hold baby in place; must never be placed near the edge of a table or counter.

   _____

2. Must be stable, not tippy; must have a strap to hold baby in; needs brakes; a package rack must be low and centered; do not use on escalators.

   _____

3. Must give baby head and neck support; needs padding and double stitching; must not pinch baby's arms and legs.

   _____

4. Don't use for a baby over 16 pounds; must be stable, not tippy; needs brakes; be sure carriage body locks securely into frame.

   _____

5. Needs padding and double stitching; be sure baby's legs aren't pinched; when using it, bend at your knees, not at your waist.

   _____

6. Must meet government standards for safety; should be crash-tested.

   _____

Baby Learning Review

Here are some statements about babies' learning. Circle *Yes* or *No* for each one.

1. Your baby will enjoy playing with pots, pans, and lids.   Yes   No

2. Your baby will be happy to look at his favorite mobile for hours at a time.   Yes   No

3. First your baby reaches for and grabs hold of swinging objects. Then she learns to swipe at them and make them move.   Yes   No

4. Even though your baby can't talk yet, she'll love being talked to and having books read to her.   Yes   No

5. Use a backpack to carry your newborn baby around and keep him close to you.   Yes   No

6. Your baby will enjoy the sound of music.   Yes   No

7. When your baby starts to stand, she may not know how to sit back down again at first.   Yes   No

8. You don't need to worry about your baby rolling over until he's at least 3 months old.   Yes   No

9. If you lay your newborn baby on her stomach, she'll hurt her neck by trying to hold up her head.   Yes   No

10. When your baby wants to try sitting up without being held in place, let him do it even though he keeps losing his balance and falling over.   Yes   No

Extra: Tell what is incorrect about each of the statements you circled *No* for.

Helping Your Toddler Learn
(Age: 1 year to 3 years)

YOUR TODDLER DEVELOPS

(These are the *average* ages at which toddlers develop certain abilities. Individual toddlers will do things at different ages.)

AGE	SKILLS	
1 year (12 months) (see chart on page 100)		
15 months	Walks with support. Feeds self with spoon. Uses two words together. Understands many simple words. Goes along with simple requests.	Builds with blocks.
18 months	Climbs onto furniture. Scribbles with crayons. Drinks well from cup. Can use verbs (*sit, come*). Starts make-believe play.	Walks up stairs. Negativism starts.
2 years	Helps dress self. Leads & follows peers. Walks up & down stairs. Uses short phrases & sentences. Plans & carries out complicated activities.	Nonstop talker. Runs & jumps.

(continued)

Age	Skills	
2½ years	Uses pronouns.	Knows colors.
	Becomes cooperative.	Asks for help.
	Holds crayon with finger & thumb.	
	Ready for toilet training.	
3 years (see chart on pages 125 and 126)		

USING THE BODY

Walking

Sometime between 9 and 18 months old, your baby will start walking. Now he's a toddler!

He starts by "cruising"— walking while holding on to furniture with one hand. One day he lets go and takes a step or two from one support to another. Pretty soon he's toddling along without needing any support.

Don't worry if your neighbor's baby started walking at 9 months and your baby is still only standing and cruising at 16 months. Babies vary *a lot* in the ages at which they start to walk.

How You Can Help. Arrange pieces of furniture so they're one or two toddler steps apart. Sit or stand a few steps away from your standing baby, open your arms, and invite him to come to you. Keep your beginning toddler barefoot if possible. He'll use his toes for balance. If he tries to toddle while wearing just socks, he's likely to slip.

Whole-Body Play

Your toddler needs a lot of physical play. She needs to use her whole body so she can learn how to control it. Your toddler needs to climb, run, crawl, jump, pull, push, and throw.

How You Can Help. Be sure your toddler has time and space for active physical play every day.

• She'll love the climbing gyms and swings at a playground.

- Let her practice climbing up and down stairs.
- Be sure she has some toys to push and pull, plus a ride-on toy.
- Give her some large, soft balls and balloons so she can practice throwing and catching.
- Let her jump and tumble on sofa and chair cushions spread out on the floor.

ACTIVITY

Toddler Body Play

Check each activity that might be good for a toddler.

_____ 1. Crawling through a play tunnel.
_____ 2. Jumping off the high-diving board.
_____ 3. Riding a bicycle.
_____ 4. Throwing and catching a beach ball.
_____ 5. Throwing and catching a baseball.
_____ 6. Riding a play horse with wheels.
_____ 7. Climbing an apple tree.
_____ 8. Playing on a swing set.
_____ 9. Climbing on a low jungle gym.

EXPLORING

Your toddler is, more than anything else, an *explorer*. He's completely absorbed in exploring *everything* in the world around him. He looks at, touches, tastes, feels, and listens to everything. And with his newfound skill of walking, he can get to all these fascinating things! (That's why making your home *safe* for your toddler is so important—see the "Your Toddler's Safety" in the first section of this book.)

You'll notice something contradictory about your little explorer. If you're working in the kitchen, she'll want to be there with you—for a while. Then she'll wander off to investigate wonderful things in the living room. In a little while, she'll be back in the kitchen with you.

She's driven by the urge to explore and be independent. She also knows that her security depends on you, her primary caregiver. So she separates herself from you for short amounts of time, then scurries back to be sure you're still there for her.

You help your toddler learn by helping her to explore while also making her feel safe.

How You Can Help. Your toddler wants lots of things to explore and experiment with. He wants to fit things together and take them apart. He wants to pour, squeeze, stack, pull, and push. Again, you don't have to rush out and buy a lot of expensive toys for your toddler. He'd be just as interested in lots of everyday things or simple toys. Try these ideas.

- *Water Play:* Splashing, pouring, bubbling.
- *Sand Play:* Pouring, digging, molding.
- *Play Dough:* Squeezing, rolling, shaping.
- *Blocks:* Stacking, tipping over, lining up, building.
- *Nesting & Fitting Play*
- *Threading*
- *Sorting*
- *Filling & Dumping*

ACTIVITY

Household Toys

Find and list here the things around your home your child could use for each of the last four activities mentioned above. Share your lists with classmates.

Nesting & Fitting	Threading	Sorting	Filling & Dumping
_____	_____	_____	_____
_____	_____	_____	_____
_____	_____	_____	_____
_____	_____	_____	_____
_____	_____	_____	_____
_____	_____	_____	_____
_____	_____	_____	_____
_____	_____	_____	_____

DRAMATIC AND CREATIVE PLAY

Imitating and Make-Believe

Your toddler exercises his imagination with "make-believe" play. He creates imaginary worlds and makes things happen in them. He pretends to be you and a variety of other people. He adopts dolls and stuffed toys as friends and companions. Here are some things you can do to help your toddler exercise his imagination:

■ **Imaginary worlds.**

Give her mini people, farm animals, cars and trucks. Add blocks and small boxes for houses, barns, garages.

■ **Dress-up.**

Give him simple items that make him be like someone else: a scarf, a hat, a purse, boots and shoes.

■ **Being you.**

Let her do what you're doing. When you're digging in the garden, give her a digging tool, too. Sponge the tabletop together. You sweep with a broom while she uses a whiskbroom.

■ **Dolls and stuffed toys.**

Be sure your toddler has some of these friends to play along with him. They'll comfort him when he's sad or lonesome. They'll be the targets of his anger, too—he'll let out some of his upset feelings by hitting and throwing them.

ACTIVITY

Toddler Toys

Here's a list of toys a toddler might enjoy using in "make-believe" play. Which, if any, of these toys do you think would be most suitible for a boy toddler? Which for a girl toddler? After you make your choices, discuss each item in class.

(continued)

	Best for Boy?	Best for Girl?
Boy doll	☐	☐
Girl doll	☐	☐
Fire engine	☐	☐
Miniature cars	☐	☐
Mini farm animals	☐	☐
Teddy bear	☐	☐
Woman's scarf	☐	☐
Man's hat	☐	☐

Music

Your toddler will enjoy listening to music, both children's songs and rhythmic "grown-up" music. He'll enjoy making music, too—from banging a spoon on a saucepan to playing a toy xylophone. While he's listening and playing, join him in marching, dancing, and clapping for a complete music experience.

Crayons and Paper

Your toddler enjoys the first stages of drawing: large crayons and felt-tip pens on paper, chalk on chalkboard, fingerpaints. She's not drawing pictures of things—she's enjoying creating lines, colors, and shapes.

LANGUAGE DEVELOPMENT

Your 1-year-old will probably be able to say a few words. He'll also be able to understand quite a few words you say. By the time he's 2, he may be able to use 200 words. He'll also speak in simple sentences, like "Me get down" and "Doggie bark." Here are some ways to help your toddler develop his language skills.

Talk to Your Toddler

Just as you did when she was a baby, your toddler needs to hear words and have them connected to things, actions, and feelings. If you're helping her put on her coat, say, "Let's put your coat on." If she's getting angry, say, "Oh, you feel mad about this, don't you?"

Listen to Your Toddler

Learning to speak can be frustrating for your toddler—and for you, too. He knows what he wants to say, but he can't quite say it so you can understand it! Listen carefully to what he's saying. The more you listen, the more you'll understand. You can tell other people what he means, too.

Ignore the Grammar

When your toddler starts to put words together, she knows nothing, about grammar. She doesn't care about the right way to speak. She just wants to get her meaning across. If you try to correct her, you'll discourage her from talking to you.

Instead of correcting your toddler, respond to her using real words and good grammar. She tells you, "I ated my nana." You respond, "Oh, good. You ate your banana." After a while, on her own, she'll pick up the right way to say things.

Read Books with Your Toddler

As with your baby, read books with your toddler. The books should be sturdy and simple with big, detailed pictures of things your toddler will recognize. Read the words, talk about the pictures. Encourage your toddler to talk about what he sees on the pages. He's learning more language and learning that reading is fun!

ACTIVITY

Toddler Talk

Which parent response is most helpful in each of these situations?

1. Toddler Charlie says, "Blerf mnuh grexl." Parent responds:
    _____ a. "Stop that, Charlie. I don't know what you're saying."
    _____ b. "What, Charlie? Do you want your shoes? Can you show me?"
2. Toddler Lauren says, "Me get down." Parent says:
    _____ a. "No, Lauren. Say, 'I want to get down.' "
    _____ b. "You want to get down, Lauren? Okay."

(continued)

3. Toddler Tran points to a crying boy in the picture book. Parent says:

_____ a. "Oh, look at the crying boy. He must feel sad."

_____ b. "Yes, see the boy."

Books for Toddlers

Go to your local library and choose some books you think toddlers would enjoy. Try these books out on some real toddlers. What features of a book do toddlers most seem to enjoy?

GOING PLACES

Your toddler is super-active, and super-interested in everything around him. You'll want to take him places so he can learn about the world outside your home. Here are some ideas for outings with your toddler:

■ Playgrounds and play groups.

Your toddler isn't ready to play *with* other children. But he can get used to playing *near* or *around* other toddlers. Try public playgrounds. Form a small play group with a few other parents of toddlers.

■ Story time and children's shows.

Your toddler will enjoy simple entertainment aimed at his age group. Check your local library and newspaper listings.

■ Daily errands.

Your toddler will love going on everyday errands with you. Make them a learning experience: "How many green things do we have in our grocery cart?"

Remember: Going places with a toddler can be hazardous to your sanity. A toddler *can't* behave "properly" for more than a few minutes. She can't be quiet and cooperative just because you tell her to be. If you take her anyplace when she's hungry, stressed, or tired, you'll have a disaster on your hands. You must expect her to be squirmy, inquisitive, talkative. If you're going somewhere people are supposed to be quiet, attentive, and well-behaved (a concert, a wedding, a fancy restaurant), *don't take your toddler*.

And, of course, follow the traffic safety rules for toddlers. (See "Your Toddler's Safety" in the first section of this book.)

Toddler Learning Review

Here are some statements about toddlers learning. Circle *Yes* or *No* for each.

1.	Your baby becomes a toddler when he starts to walk.	Yes	No
2.	Your toddler will love playing with water and sand.	Yes	No
3.	Your toddler, busy exploring, stays away from you for long periods of time.	Yes	No
4.	Boy toddlers do not enjoy playing with dolls.	Yes	No
5.	Your toddler will play alongside other children rather than with them.	Yes	No
6.	Your toddler wants to speak correctly and use good grammar.	Yes	No
7.	Your toddler can't be quiet and well-behaved, so don't take her with you on your daily errands.	Yes	No
8.	It's best for your toddler to walk barefoot, not in socks.	Yes	No
9.	Your toddler could hurt himself, so don't let him go up and down stairs on his own.	Yes	No
10.	Your toddler is a tireless explorer.	Yes	No

Extra: Tell what is incorrect about each of the statements you circled *No* for.

Helping Your Preschool and Kindergarten Child Learn
(Age: 3 years to 5 years)

YOUR PRESCHOOL AND KINDERGARTEN CHILD DEVELOPS

(These are the *average* ages at which young children develop certain abilities. Individual young children will do things at different ages.)

AGE	SKILLS
3 years	Dresses self in simple clothing. Can tell about something that happened. Jumps several inches. Remembers events & places. Sorts everything into categories. Knows own name & sex. Worries about body injuries. Starts playing with other children. Has an imaginary playmate. Has trouble telling fantasy from reality.
4 years	Dresses & undresses self with little help. Uses scissors to cut. Plays collective games with other children. Rides a tricycle. Skips & hops on one foot. Shapes clay or draws to resemble real things. Very self-centered: sees things from own viewpoint. Likes to boast & be bossy. Loves new things & experiences. Is exuberant & enthusiastic.

(continued)

Age	Skills
5 years	Can do small errands outside the home alone.
	Is calm & collected.
	Is easy to get along with & well-adjusted.
	Likes familiar places & things.
	Knows limits of own abilities.
	Accepts small responsibilities willingly.
	Can skate, climb trees, swing, skip with alternating feet.
	Prints some letters & numbers.
	Looks at books alone, may read some words.

DEVELOPING LARGE MOTOR SKILLS

Your preschool and kindergarten child is very physical. She's gained control of her body. Now she wants to use it. She wants to become strong and skilled. She needs to practice lots of running, jumping, climbing, hopping, kicking, throwing, catching. These are called "large motor skills."

Both boys and girls needs lots of physical play to develop strong, skilled bodies. Your young child feels good about herself when she becomes physically skilled.

ACTIVITY

Physical Activity for Young Children

Here are some situations involving young children and physical activity. Circle *Yes* or *No* for each one.

1. Kerry wants her preschooler to do well when he starts school. So she makes sure he has lots more mental activity—like doing puzzles and looking at books— than physical activity.   Yes   No

2. Steve has just chosen a preschool for his daughter. It's brightly decorated and has lots of books and art materials. The children seem happy, although there's very little room for them to run around.

                                                                 Yes   No

(continued)

3. Sharon keeps her 5-year-old off the big slide and tall jungle gym at the park so he won't get hurt.   Yes   No

4. The other tenants in the apartment building don't like noise. Jerrell takes his kids outside a lot to run and shout.   Yes   No

5. It's too difficult to dress all the kids at the pre-school to go out in the rain and snow. The kids only go out when the weather is warm and dry.   Yes   No

DEVELOPING SMALL MOTOR SKILLS

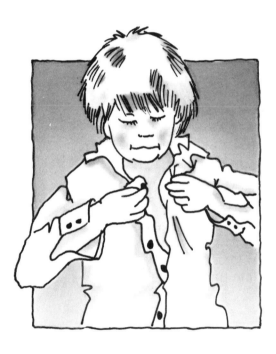

Your preschool and kindergarten child works hard at improving her running, jumping, and climbing skills. She also needs to improve her "small motor skills"—her ability to use her hands and fingers well. Here are some ways to help her develop these skills.

Dressing

Your young child can dress herself—*if* you give her the right kind of clothes. She needs large zippers and big buttons. Pull-over shirts and pants with elastic waist-bands are best. Belt buckles and snaps will be too hard for her to handle.

Drawing and Coloring

Give your young child lots of practice in drawing and coloring with large crayons and fat pencils. As he gets skilled with using these, give him thinner crayons and pencils. He's developing the hand and finger muscles he'll need when he learns to write.

Small Toys

Your young child needs to practice using smaller toys than your toddler could handle. Try puzzles, small blocks, lacing toys, small cars. If a small toy is too difficult for your young child to use, put it away for a while. Bring it out again when her small-motor skills have gotten better.

ACTIVITY

Hand and Finger Skills

Circle the items that would be helpful in developing a preschool or kindergarten child's hand and finger skills.

Large blocks

Jigsaw puzzles

Fat felt-tip markers

Beach ball

Shirts that button up the front

Small, connecting plastic building blocks

Jeans with a zipper & snap

Pull-on pants

Pullover windbreaker

CREATIVE PLAY

Your preschool and kindergarten child enjoys all kinds of creative play. He explores materials. He tries creative ideas. He's learning to express himself by creating images. He feels excited and proud about his creations.

> *Important:* Your young child probably isn't creating an image of a real thing. So don't ask, "Is that a dog?" She won't understand. She was creating an interesting shape with bright colors. Don't you know that? she wonders. Is she *supposed* to try to make a dog? she worries.

You can encourage your young child to be creative by talking about what her creation *looks like*, instead of asking her what it's supposed to *be*. Say, "What an interesting shape" or "I like those colors."

Give your preschool and kindergarten child the chance to try these creative activities, often:

■ Drawing and painting.

Water-washable felt-tip pens, crayons, colored chalk, fingerpaints, washable water-based paint. Newsprint, cheap drawing paper, rolls of wrapping paper, clipboards, easels, fat brushes.

■ **Modeling dough and clay.**

■ **Collage.**

A *collage* is a creation of cutout shapes and small objects glued to a background piece. Some items your child could glue: cutout pictures from magazines, toothpicks, fabric scraps.

■ **Tools.**

Child-sized hammers, saws, screwdrivers, nails, screws, plus blocks of scrap wood.

■ **Music.**

Keep up with the music activities your toddler enjoyed. Your young child can learn to use a child's record player. He'll enjoy singing simple songs, too.

ACTIVITY

Homemade Modeling Dough

Make your own modeling dough using this recipe:

2 cups flour

1 cup salt

1 tablespoon salad oil

1 cup water

If the dough is too sticky, add some more flour. Add food coloring or water-based paint to the water to color each batch if you want. Store in a zip-locking plastic bag or a plastic container with tight-fitting lid. Try using the dough yourself. Give it to a preschool or kindergarten child to use, too.

Collage Materials

Make a collection of materials you find around your home that a young child could use in making a collage. Bring your collection to class to show to classmates.

DRAMATIC PLAY

Your toddler enjoyed *acting like* someone else. Your preschool and kindergarten child spends a lot of time *being* someone else. Give her some props and let her imagination take off! An umbrella can be a sword (she's a knight) or a magic wand (she's a wizard). Hats transform her into a baseball player, a detective, an airline pilot. Cardboard cartons, large blocks, and old pillows create a house, a school, a hospital room. A bedsheet or blanket over a table makes her a camper with a tent.

Imaginary Friends

Many preschool children have an imaginary playmate. This friend exists only in your young child's mind. You can't see "Amy." But your young child talks to her and tells you, "Watch out! You're about to sit on Amy!"

Don't worry. Your young child isn't learning to tell lies. He's just exercising his imagination and being creative in yet another way. When your young child gets a little older, "Amy" will disappear. You may even miss her!

LANGUAGE DEVELOPMENT

Your preschool and kindergarten child uses language very well—almost as well as an adult. He makes some mistakes in grammar, of course. He doesn't pronounce every word correctly, but he knows a tremendous number of words. Here's how to keep your young child's language skills developing.

Two-Way Talk

When your young child speaks to you, *listen* to what she's saying. Then *respond* to her. You give her new words. You encourage her to talk and express her ideas. She says, "Can't reach!" You respond, "You can't reach that shelf, can you? It's too high. You're not tall enough." You've given her words for *shelf* and the ideas of *high* and *tall*.

Pronouns and Grammar

Pronouns (words like *I*, *me*, *you*, *him*, *she*) are very confusing for your young child. So she doesn't say, "You come with me." Instead, she says,

"Daddy come with Annie." Help her get used to how pronouns are used by responding, "Okay. I'll come with you." Eventually she'll get it.

In the same way, your young child will use incorrect grammar: "Annie goed to store." Help her by responding the right way: "Oh, so you went to the store today." Don't tell her she's wrong. Just say it right.

"Why?" Questions

Your young child is brimming with curiosity. He wants to know *everything*. Around the age of 3, your young child will start asking "Why?" about almost everything. "Why is the sky blue? Why are clouds? Why am I Brian?" Each answer you give is likely to lead to another question.

The 50th (or 20th) "Why?" question of the day may make you want to scream. Don't! "Why?" questions show that your child is eager to learn. Keep him eager and learning by answering the questions. Try these ways of dealing with "Why?" questions:

- Give a brief answer, if you have one.
- Tell him a little more about the subject, if you can.
- If you don't know, say you can both look for the answer in a book.
- Turn the question back on him: "Why do you think?"
- End a whole string of "Why?" questions by changing to another interesting subject or activity.

ACTIVITY

"Why?" Role-Play

With a classmate, role-play a "Why?" question scene. The "parent" starts off with a simple statement like, "It's time for lunch now," or, "It's raining out." The "child" responds, "Why?" The string of "Why?"'s goes on for a while. Then the "parent" uses one of the "Why?" question tips to end the scene.

Books

Continue to keep your preschool and kindergarten child interested in books. Books will be very important to her when she starts elementary school.

Have lots of picture books around your home for your young child to look at, on her own and with you. Talking about the pictures helps her get ready for real reading.

Read story books with lots of pictures to your young child, too. As you read, she looks at the pictures that *show* the words you're saying. This also helps your young child get ready to read on her own.

ACTIVITY

Books for Young Children

Go to your local library. Find some books for preschool and kindergarten children. Try the books out on some real preschool and kindergarten children. What features of a book do these kids most seem to enjoy?

_____

_____

_____

Be an Author

Write a children's story yourself. Then illustrate it, or have an artistic friend illustrate it. Share your creation with your classmates.

AROUND THE HOME

Your preschool and kindergarten child is ready to help around the home. She can *help* to clean her room. (The room is probably very messy by day's end. She'll need some help. You could say, I'll put the books on the shelf. You put the blocks in the box.")

Give your young child a few simple household chores. He can put his dirty clothes in the laundry basket. He can empty the bedroom wastebaskets into the garbage can. He can set the table or wipe it off. Doing household chores makes your child feel responsible and grown up.

ACTIVITY

Household Chores

What other household chores could a preschool or kindergarten child do? Write a list of chores you might reasonably expect a young child to do in the course of a week. Compare your list with classmates' lists.

GOING PLACES

Outings with your preschool and kindergarten child are a delight compared with daily trips with your toddler. Your young child can help get things off the store's shelves. She can suggest items you've left off your shopping list. She won't often scream for you to buy her a toy or candy.

Your young child is much less likely than your toddler to get fussy or whiny on outings. Now is the time for "field trips." Here are some ideas for educational and fun places to take your preschool and kindergarten child:

- Zoos
- Farms
- Children's museums
- Aquariums
- Food-processing plants
- Playgrounds

As always, whenever you take your young child in a car, be sure to strap her into a child safety seat.

ACTIVITY

Places to Go with Your Young Child

Make a list of public places in your community where you could take your preschool or kindergarten child for a fun outing. If you don't have a car, how would you get to each of these places?

_____

_____

_____

_____

_____

Preschool and Kindergarten Learning Review

Here are some statements about young children learning. Circle *Yes* or *No* for each one.

1. Mental development is more important for a young child than physical development.   Yes   No

2. Your young child asks all those "Why?" questions because he knows it annoys you.   Yes   No

3. Your young child needs to develop both "small motor" and "large motor" skills.   Yes   No

4. When your young child creates an imaginary play-mate, it's a sign that she's disturbed about life.   Yes   No

5. Your young child isn't likely to get very fussy or whiny on outings with you.   Yes   No

6. Your young child will enjoy creating accurate pictures of real things.   Yes   No

7. You can depend on your young child to clean his room on his own.   Yes   No

8. Your young child can have trouble telling what's real from what's fantasy.   Yes   No

9. Preschool and kindergarten boys need more physical play than preschool and kindergarten girls do.   Yes   No

10. Your young child loves to pretend that she's someone else.   Yes   No

Extra: Tell what is incorrect about each of the statements you circled *No* for.

```
┌─────────────────────────────────────┐
│                                     │
│                  V                  │
│                                     │
│          CHOOSING AND               │
│          USING CHILD                │
│             CARE                    │
│                                     │
└─────────────────────────────────────┘
```

REASONS FOR USING SUBSTITUTE CARE

All parents need someone else to look after their children sometimes. "Substitute care" may mean a babysitter for an hour or two while you go out. Or it may mean all-day care while you work a full-time job.

Years ago, most mothers stayed home and cared for their children full-time. This is not so common in today's world. Here's why most families now need at least some substitute care—someone else to look after their children:

- Both parents have jobs outside the home, because:

    —The family needs two incomes.
    —The mother (as well as the father) wants and needs a profession, a career.
    —The mother (as well as the father) would feel dissatisfied and unhappy staying at home all the time with small children.

- A single parent has to have a job to support the family.

All of these are perfectly good reasons to use substitute care for your child. You're not a bad parent if someone else looks after your child while you work. Just be sure to choose your caregiver and day-care center carefully. Here's how.

A CAREGIVER'S CHARACTER

You've decided you need substitute care for your baby or young child. What kind of a person should you look for? Try these ideas:

- A warm, loving, happy person. (She needs to give your baby or young child the affection he needs all day long that he'd otherwise get from you.)

- A person who enjoys babies and young children, and is interested in them. (She'll be responsive to your baby/young child—which is *very* important for his development.)

- A person whom you like and can talk to easily.

- A person who has the same ideas about raising children as you do.

- A person who knows something about the social, emotional, and developmental needs of babies and young children.

ACTIVITY

Whom Would You Choose?

Which of these caregivers would you choose to care for your baby or young child? What problems do you think you might experience with each one?

1. Caregiver A is very sensible, has lots of experience, and knows all the experts' ideas about child-rearing. She doesn't have much of a sense of humor and seems to avoid physical contact.

   Would you choose Caregiver A? Why or why not?

2. Caregiver B thinks children should be allowed to follow their natural instincts in almost everything they do. You think children need to be carefully guided so they learn self-control and how to get along socially.

   Would you choose Caregiver B? Why or why not?

3. Caregiver C uses poor grammar, her home is rather untidy, and she never graduated from high school. Her kids are clean and full of life, and she obviously enjoys interacting with them.

   Would you choose Caregiver C? Why or why not?

Role-Play

With a classmate, role-play a parent interviewing a potential caregiver. The parent is trying to find out something about the kind of person the caregiver is.

TYPES OF SUBSTITUTE CARE

The Other Parent

This isn't really "substitute" care, of course. Here are some ways it works:

- One parent works outside the home. The other parent takes care of the child at home.

- Parents arrange their work schedules so one of them is home with the child most of the time. Parents work full-time or part-time.

- A mother gets *maternity leave* from her job to stay home with a new baby for a certain number of weeks or months. Or a father gets *paternity leave*. The leave may be paid, partly paid, or unpaid.

A Relative or Neighbor

- A relative comes to your home, or you take your child to the relative's home.

- A neighbor looks after your child in her home.

A Caregiver in Your Home

- You hire a person to come to your home to take care of your child.

Family Day Care

- Another parent takes care of your child plus her own and a few others in her home.

Family day care may be licensed by the city or state. Family day care may also be unlicensed.

Day-Care Center

- Day-care centers provide group care for young children whose parents work.

  Day-care centers are like family day care: children eat, sleep, and play there. Day-care centers are like nursery schools: Trained staff members offer educational activities to the children.

  Day-care centers can be private, for-profit. Some are non-profit, run by government or social service agencies. A few larger employers run day-care centers for their employees' children.

Play Group

- Several parents take turns getting their young children together in each other's homes for group play.

  Play groups usually meet for a few hours in the morning, several days each week. Play groups give young children a chance to play alongside each other and learn about being in a group.

Nursery School

- Children 3 and 4 years old spend half a day at a "pre-kindergarten" program.

  Staff members are trained in early childhood education and child development. Nursery school emphasizes creative and cooperative activities.

  A cooperative nursery school is run by parents who hire a teacher and take turns being the teacher's assistants. Head Start is a nursery school program that's paid for by the federal government. It's for children from low-income families, to help them be ready for public school.

Kindergarten

- Children 5 and 6 years old start getting ready for elementary school by going to kindergarten for half a day, five days a week.

Children whose parents both work may go to a day-care center for the half of the day when they're not at kindergarten.

Most states offer free, public kindergarten. Private and parent-run cooperative kindergartens also exist.

ACTIVITY

What Kind of Care?

Here are some situations when parents need some substitute care for their baby or young child. If you were the parent in each case, which type of substitute care would you choose? Write the name of one of the eight types of care in the space after each situation.

other parent	play group	kindergarten
relative/neighbor	day-care center	family day care
caregiver in your home	nursery school	

1. You want your 2-year-old to start learning about playing with other children.

   _____

2. Both you and your spouse have full-time jobs during the day. You need to arrange care for your 5-year-old.

   _____

3. You're a single parent with a full-time job during the day. You need to arrange care for your 2-year-old.

   _____

4. You're about to have a baby. You're going back to work 6 weeks after the baby's born.

   _____

5. You think it would be good for your 4-year-old to spend time with other children and do some educational activities.

   _____

6. Your spouse works from 3 p.m. to 11 p.m. weekdays. You're looking for a job and deciding what kind of care to get for your 1-year-old.

How to Use Substitute Care

Separate Gradually

Don't just dump your child and run off. Chat with the caregiver for a minute or two, help your child off with his coat, say goodbye. You're giving him a little time to adjust to the new setting.

When your child is just starting day care, plan to stay for a while. Let her know when you leave, and tell her you'll be back. Once your child is used to day care, she may still fuss and cry as you leave. This is normal, as long as the caregiver lets you know that your child settles down happily soon after you've left.

Leave Phone Numbers

Give the caregiver phone numbers where you and other family members can be reached. Give the caregiver instructions about what to do in an emergency. Be sure you both know what's supposed to happen in case of emergency.

Stay Involved

You are still responsible.

When you pick up your child or get home, talk to the child about his day. What happened? What advances and triumphs did he experience? What problems came up?

Visit your child's care center at times. Watch what's going on. Volunteer to help out when you can.

Stay in Charge

An older or more experienced caregiver—especially an older relative—may try to take over. Be assertive! Final decisions about how your child is to be raised belong to *you*.

Spend "Quality" Time with Your Child

Since you can't spend quantities of time with your child, spend "quality" time with her instead. This means you pay complete attention to your child during your time together that's going to be "quality" time.

HOW TO CHOOSE A SUBSTITUTE CARE CENTER OR HOME

You may take your baby or young child to a neighbor's home, a family day-care home, or a group-care center. Here are some things to consider when you're choosing a day-care home or center.

Look the place over. Ask yourself these questions (you want a *yes* answer):

- Is it clean? Does it smell clean?
- Is it safe and healthy for your active baby? for your exploring toddler? for your rambunctious preschooler?
- Is food stored properly? Are milk and formula kept in the refrigerator? Are bottles and nipples properly clean?

Talk to the person in charge. Ask these questions;

- "What do the children eat for lunch? For snacks?" (Meals should be a good mix of foods from the four food groups. Snacks should be healthy. See Section II, on "Nutrition."
- "Do the children play outside for part of each day if the weather allows that?" (They need to be outdoors.)
- "Can I drop in at any time?" (If the answer is no, *do not* choose this center or home.)
- "How many babies and children do you take care of? How many adults do you have to take care of them?" (See the individual sections that follow for information on how many adults are needed per baby, per toddler, and per preschool or kindergarten child.)
- "How long has each caregiver been working here? Do you expect them to stay with the job for several years?" (Babies and young children need to develop a close relationship with their main caregiver. They'll be upset if the person who cares for them most of the time disappears. So you don't want caregivers to change very often.)
- "What kind of training and experience does each worker have?" (You want well-trained or at least experienced caregivers.)
- "Will anyone else besides the people I've met be in charge of the children at times?" (You need to know and check out every adult who will be alone with your baby or child.)

Watch the caregivers with the babies and children. Ask yourself these questions (again, you want a *yes* answer):

- Do the caregivers seem to like and understand babies and young children?

- Is each child treated as an individual and given individual care and attention?

- Are the children guided in positive ways—by praise, smiles, and pats? Are the children *not* shamed, scolded, punished, and told "No, no" all the time?

When you're choosing a day-care center or home, make an appointment to check it out. You might arrive early. This way, you can see how things normally are, when visitors are not expected.

If you like the center or home, go back with your baby or young child. See how your child responds to the center. See how the staff members respond to your child.

Remember, *you* are hiring *them*. They are not hiring you. Resist any feeling that you must settle for care you don't feel comfortable with. Try to keep looking until you find a place that suits you.

ACTIVITY

What's Your Choice?

Here are some descriptions of substitute-care centers or homes. Which ones would you choose for your child? Write Yes or No next to each description.

_____ 1. The babies' lunch bottles are prepared and waiting on the kitchen counter by mid-morning.

_____ 2. Two of the caregivers have worked at the center for three years. The third caregiver has been there for a year and a half.

_____ 3. The caregiver assures you that your child will fit right in because the center has four other children her age and "all 3-year-olds are alike."

_____ 4. The caregiver says you should not drop in unannounced during the day because this disturbs the routine and upsets the children.

_____ 5. Whenever a baby cries, one of the caregivers picks the baby up.

_____ 6. Whenever a toddler pushes a playmate, that toddler is told he's being bad and has to stand in the corner for 10 minutes.

(continued)

_____ 7. The toddlers' exploring area is separate from the older children's very active play area.

_____ 8. The children play outside even when it's quite cold.

THE SICK CHILD AND DAY CARE

Once your child starts any kind of group day care, he'll probably start having colds and other illnesses quite often, at least for the first year or so. You'll have to decide how to handle your child's sick-at-home days. Can you or your spouse stay home with your child? Can you line up a backup babysitter to call on when your child is sick?

When can your sick child go back to day care? Your day-care center or home may have its own rules about this. A general guideline would be:

- If your child has a common cold (runny nose, mild cough, slightly sore throat), she can go to day care.
- If your child has a fever (temperature of 100°F or more), is vomiting, or has diarrhea, she must stay home.
- If your child has chicken pox, see page 35.

Substitute Care for Your Baby
(Age: Birth to 1 year)

Your baby needs *lots* of attention. She learns to trust other people and to feel like a valuable human being when her caregiver responds promptly and lovingly to her. So look for these qualities in substitute care for your baby (as well as "yes" answers to the checklist on page 141).

ONE CAREGIVER, ONE BABY?

- One caregiver for one baby is ideal. For example: a parent, a relative, a neighbor, or a paid caregiver in your home.

- Family day care is also good for babies. *Be sure* a caregiver is caring for only two babies at a time (and for no more than four children altogether under the age of 5).

- In an infant-care center, be sure there are *two* caregivers for every four or five babies.

MEETING YOUR BABY'S NEEDS

To be sure your baby-care home or center is meeting your baby's needs, you need a "yes" answer to each of these questions.

- Is your baby being stimulated? Does she have things to look at, reach for, and touch? Are these things changed often?

- Is your baby picked up often? He needs to be held and cuddled a lot, not just when he's being fed.

- Does the caregiver talk to your baby a lot? Does she speak real words, in full sentences? Your baby learns to talk by listening to her caregivers talk to her.

- Does the caregiver give your baby lots of affection?

- Does your baby get outdoors for a while most days?

- Does the caregiver use positive guidance—smiles, cuddles, praise instead of "No, no"?

- Does the caregiver *never* punish your baby?

Substitute Care for Your Toddler
(Age: 1 year to 3 years)

Toddlers are explorers. They need safe, stimulating surroundings to be active in. So look for these qualities in substitute care for your toddler (as well as "yes" answers to the checklist on page 141).

- Room to practice walking and running.
- Many objects to explore by sighht, touch, climbing, crawling, filling, emptying, fitting, taking apart.
- Equipment for creative play—like art, music, cars and dolls, building.
- A roomful of happy activity, but not overstimulated hyperactivity.
- Corners for quiet, individual play and naps.
- Lots of books.
- No more than four or five children under the age of 5 for a single caregiver. If there are two caregivers, no more than six to eight children altogether.
- Toddlers playing individually, perhaps alongside each other. Each toddler with the space, equipment, and freedom to do what interests him at that moment.
- Very little, if any, use of TV.

Remember that these are the "terrible twos." Your child is fighting for independence and often is very contrary and negative. You may long for a period of close togetherness at the end of your work day. Your toddler may want just the opposite. Relax and accept the mood he's in right now.

Substitute Care for Your Preschool and Kindergarten Child
(Age: 3 years to 5 years)

Your preschooler is ready for group play, and your kindergarten child is getting more skilled at playing with other children. Your preschool/kindergarten child needs lots of physical activity, too, to develop his body and muscle coordination. So look for these qualities in substitute care for your preschool and kindergarten child (as well as "yes" answers to the checklist on page 141).

- Room and time for very active play—running, shouting, climbing, tumbling.
- Materials for make-believe and creative, dramatic play.
- Learning centers—areas where your young child can experiment with different creative and learning supplies.
- Art and music activities.
- Staff members trained in early childhood education.
- Group play that is cooperative, not competitive.
- Free-play periods as well as group-play periods.
- Very little, if any, use of television.
- Lots of books.
- Parent-teacher conferences once or twice a year.
- No more than eight children per caregiver.

ACTIVITY

Real-Life Observation

Visit several different substitute-care centers and homes. Using our checklists, rate each center or home as good, adequate, or unacceptable for babies, for toddlers, and for preschool and kindergarten children. Share your findings with classmates.

Substitute Care Review

Here are some qualities of substitute-care centers or homes. Decide which age group each quality is best suited for. Write baby, toddler, and/or preschool/kindergarten after each.

1. One caregiver for every eight children. _____

2. No punishment, ever. _____

3. Lots of books. _____

4. Lots of room for running. _____

5. Quiet space for naps. _____

6. Lots of affection and cuddling. _____

7. One caregiver looking after no more than two of this age group.

   _____

8. Lots of objects to explore. _____

9. Very little, if any, use of TV. _____

10. Learning centers. _____

11. Things to look at, reach for, and touch. _____

12. Individual play time. _____